GOLDEN BELLS

HOMER A. RODEHEAVER
Compiler

CHAS. H. GABRIEL
Music Editor

FOR CHURCH, SUNDAY SCHOOL AND EVANGELISTIC SERVICES

REVIVAL SONGS
CHILDREN'S SONGS
SONGS FOR MALE VOICES
SOLOS AND CHORUSES
CHURCH HYMNS
SPIRITUALS

PRICES

Manila, wire stitched, single copy, postpaid, . .20c
Any quantity, not prepaid, per copy, . . . 15c

The RODEHEAVER
HALL-MACK Co.

28 East Jackson Boulevard
CHICAGO

124 North Fifteenth Street
PHILADELPHIA

C

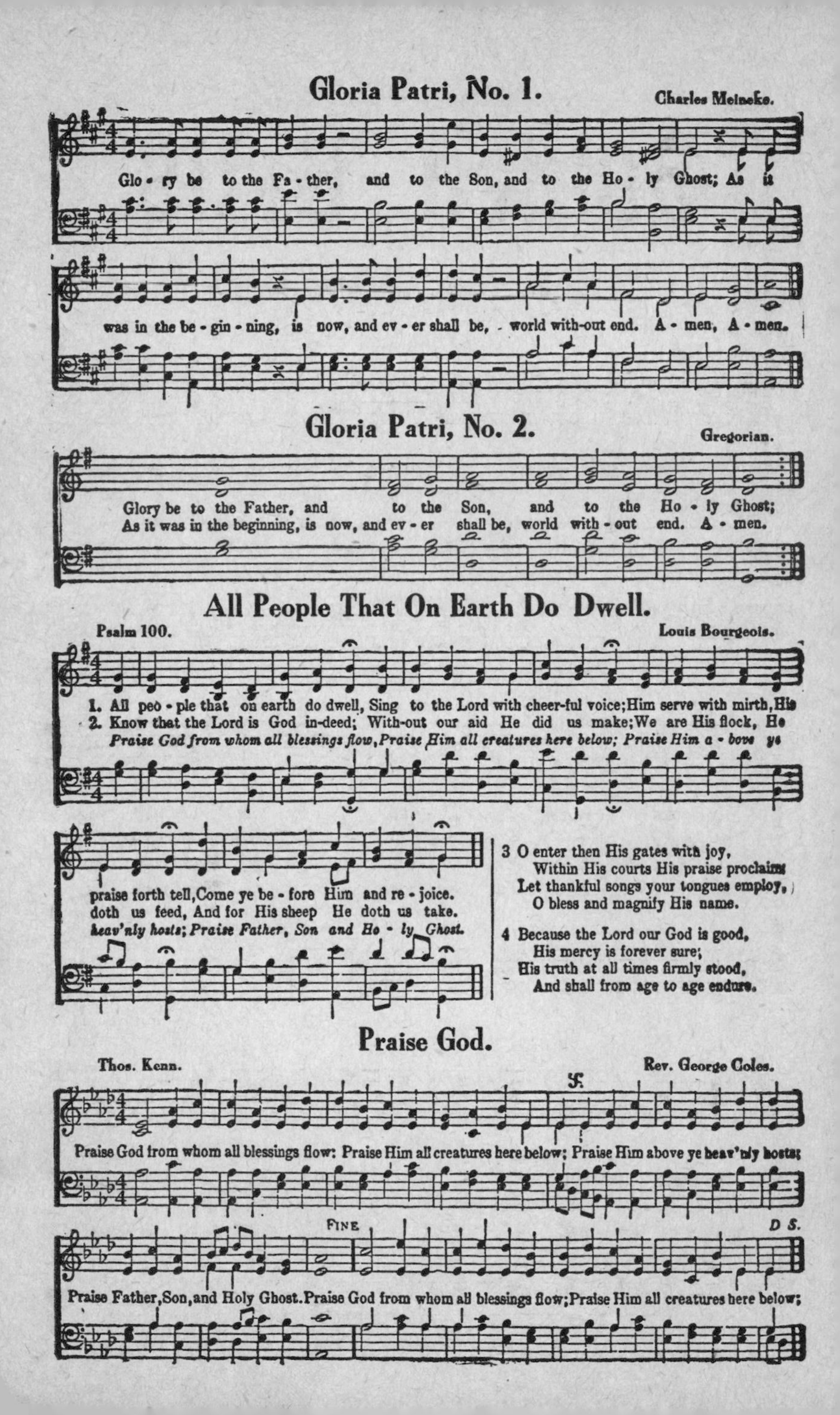

Gloria Patri, No. 1.
Charles Meineke.
Glo - ry be to the Fa - ther, and to the Son, and to the Ho - ly Ghost; As it
was in the be - gin - ning, is now, and ev - er shall be, - world with-out end. A - men, A - men.
Gloria Patri, No. 2.
Gregorian.
Glory be to the Father, and to the Son, and to the Ho - ly Ghost;
As it was in the beginning, is now, and ev - er shall be, world with - out end. A - men.
All People That On Earth Do Dwell.
Psalm 100.
Louis Bourgeois.
1. All peo - ple that on earth do dwell, Sing to the Lord with cheer-ful voice; Him serve with mirth, His praise forth tell, Come ye be - fore Him and re - joice.
2. Know that the Lord is God in-deed; With-out our aid He did us make; We are His flock, He doth us feed, And for His sheep He doth us take.
Praise God from whom all blessings flow, Praise Him all creatures here below; Praise Him a - bove ye heav'nly hosts; Praise Father, Son and Ho - ly Ghost.
3 O enter then His gates with joy,
Within His courts His praise proclaim;
Let thankful songs your tongues employ,
O bless and magnify His name.
4 Because the Lord our God is good,
His mercy is forever sure;
His truth at all times firmly stood,
And shall from age to age endure.
Praise God.
Thos. Kenn.
Rev. George Coles.
Praise God from whom all blessings flow: Praise Him all creatures here below; Praise Him above ye heav'nly hosts;
FINE
D.S.
Praise Father, Son, and Holy Ghost. Praise God from whom all blessings flow; Praise Him all creatures here below;

Golden Bells.

1 Come, Thou Almighty King.

Charles Wesley. Felice Giardini.

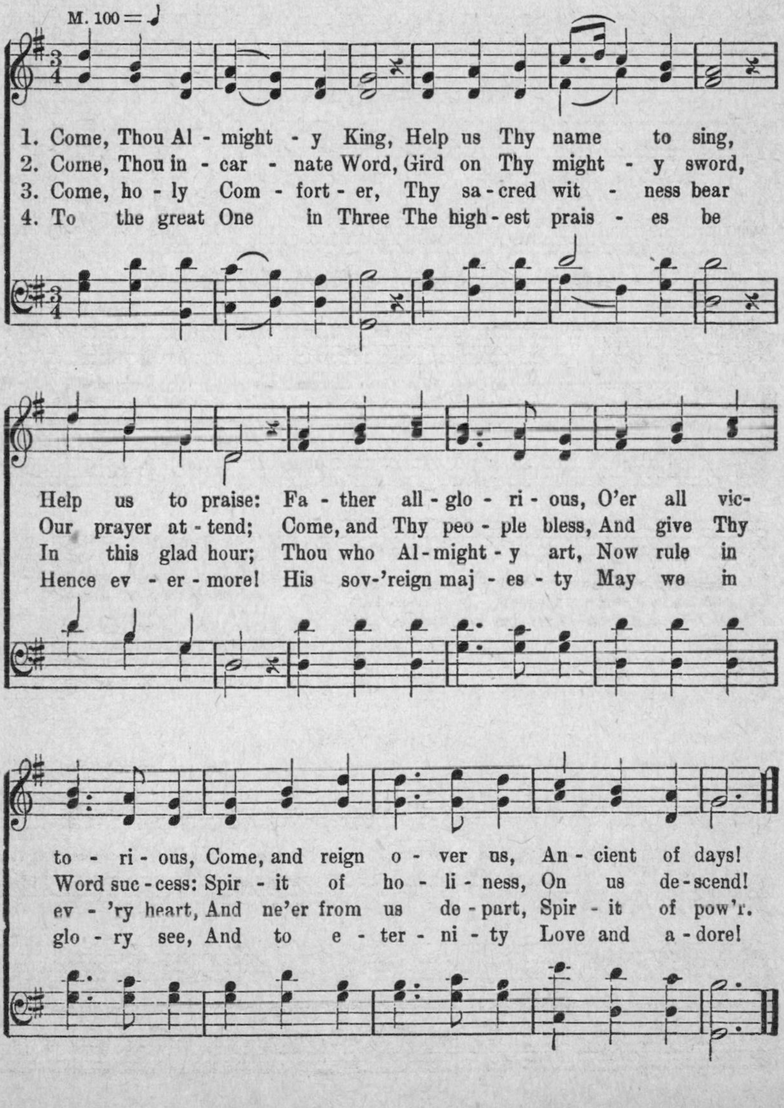

M. 100 = ♩

1. Come, Thou Al - might - y King, Help us Thy name to sing,
2. Come, Thou in - car - nate Word, Gird on Thy might - y sword,
3. Come, ho - ly Com - fort - er, Thy sa - cred wit - ness bear
4. To the great One in Three The high - est prais - es be

Help us to praise: Fa - ther all - glo - ri - ous, O'er all vic-
Our prayer at - tend; Come, and Thy peo - ple bless, And give Thy
In this glad hour; Thou who Al - might - y art, Now rule in
Hence ev - er - more! His sov-'reign maj - es - ty May we in

to - ri - ous, Come, and reign o - ver us, An - cient of days!
Word suc - cess: Spir - it of ho - li - ness, On us de - scend!
ev - 'ry heart, And ne'er from us de - part, Spir - it of pow'r.
glo - ry see, And to e - ter - ni - ty Love and a - dore!

The Song of Triumph.

Ina Duley Ogdon. Chas. H. Gabriel.

M. 100
1. When we meet to-geth - er on the oth - er shore, When the jour-ney's
2. Of His mer-cy shall our grate-ful an-them roll, On re - un - ion
3. When at last we know Him and His name shall own, When His king-dom
cares and its dan-gers shall be o'er; When our eyes be-hold our
day in the home-land of the soul; Heav-en's might-y arch - es with
com - eth and He is on His throne, When the liv - ing treas - ures
FINE.
Sav - ior, Lord and King— What a song of tri - umph we shall sing!
mel - o - dy shall ring— What a song of tri - umph we shall sing!
for His crown we bring— What a song of tri - umph we shall sing!
D. S.—Life's e - ter-nal spring, What a song of tri-umph we shall sing!
CHORUS.
There's a song A hap-py song, ev-'ry-bod-y will sing, One of praise glo - ry, laud and praise,
D.S.
un - to Je - sus the King! With the ransomed host of Zi - on at

3.

I Must Tell Jesus.

E. A. H. COPYRIGHT. 1893, BY THE HOFFMAN MUSIC CO. Rev. E. A. Hoffman.

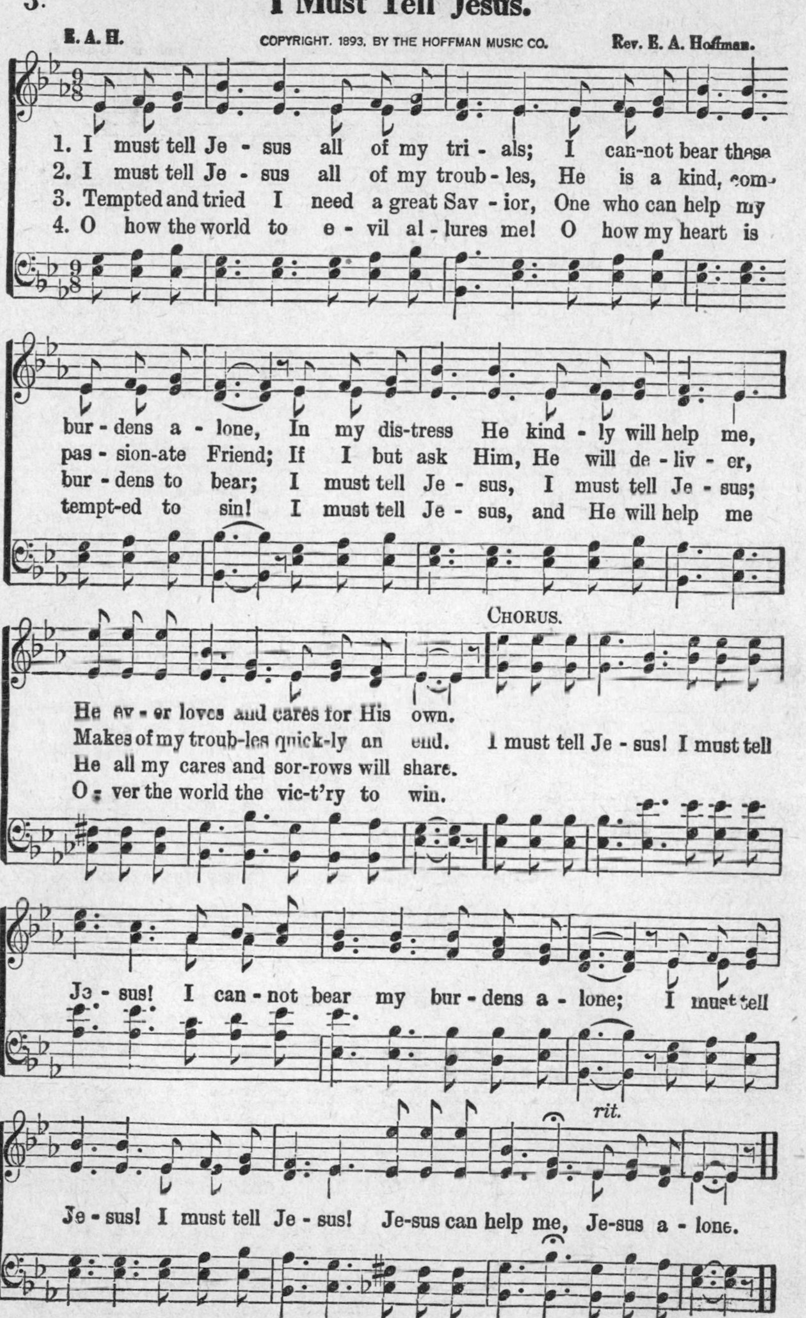
1. I must tell Je - sus all of my tri - als; I can-not bear these
2. I must tell Je - sus all of my troub - les, He is a kind, com-
3. Tempted and tried I need a great Sav - ior, One who can help my
4. O how the world to e - vil al - lures me! O how my heart is
bur - dens a - lone, In my dis-tress He kind - ly will help me,
pas - sion-ate Friend; If I but ask Him, He will de - liv - er,
bur - dens to bear; I must tell Je - sus, I must tell Je - sus;
tempt-ed to sin! I must tell Je - sus, and He will help me
He ev - er loves and cares for His own.
Makes of my troub-les quick-ly an end.
He all my cares and sor-rows will share.
O - ver the world the vic-t'ry to win.
CHORUS.
I must tell Je - sus! I must tell
Je - sus! I can - not bear my bur - dens a - lone; I must tell
Je - sus! I must tell Je - sus! Je-sus can help me, Je-sus a - lone.
rit.

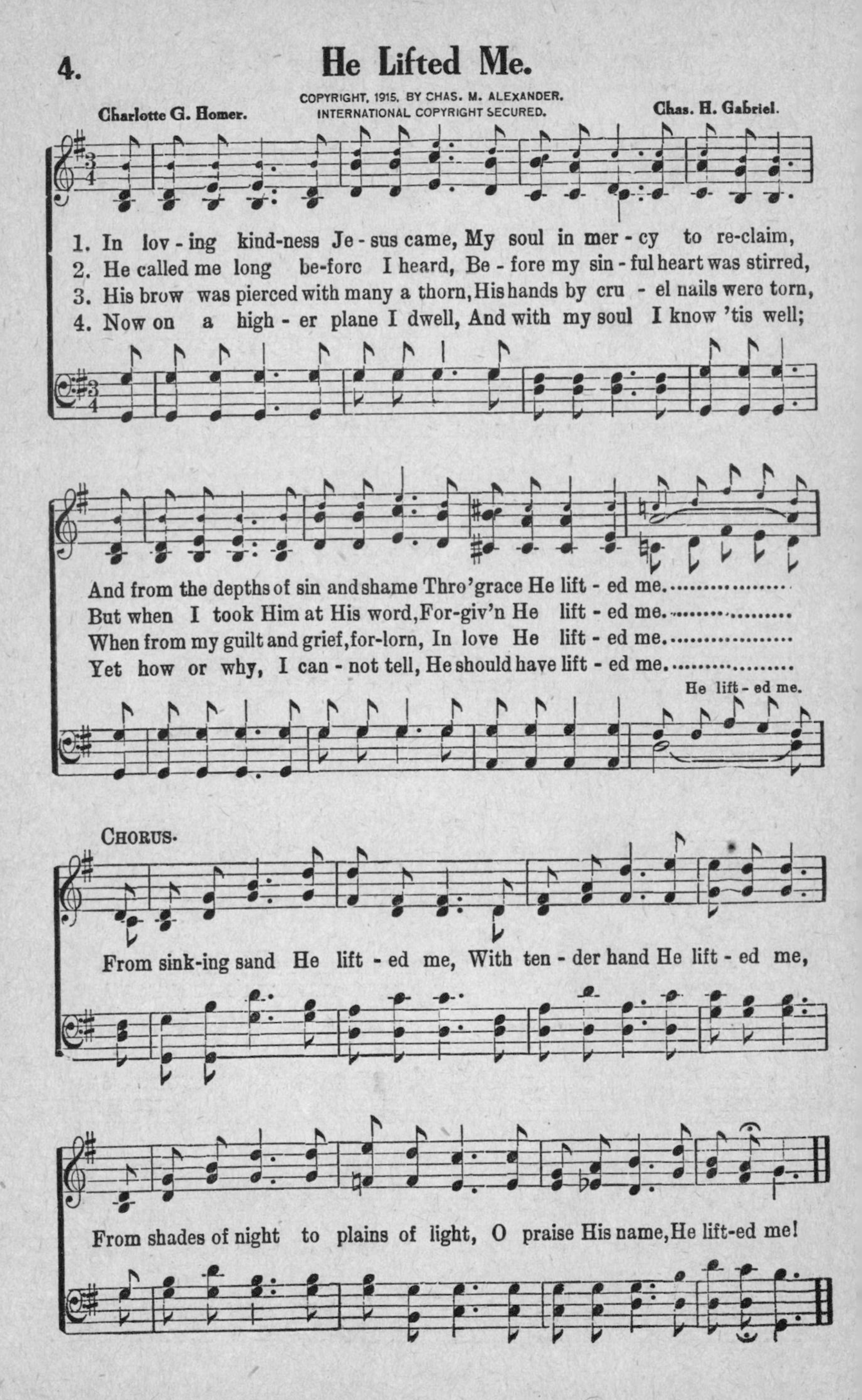
4.
He Lifted Me.
COPYRIGHT, 1915, BY CHAS. M. ALEXANDER.
INTERNATIONAL COPYRIGHT SECURED.
Charlotte G. Homer.
Chas. H. Gabriel.
1. In lov - ing kind-ness Je - sus came, My soul in mer - cy to re-claim,
2. He called me long be-fore I heard, Be - fore my sin - ful heart was stirred,
3. His brow was pierced with many a thorn, His hands by cru - el nails were torn,
4. Now on a high - er plane I dwell, And with my soul I know 'tis well;
And from the depths of sin and shame Thro' grace He lift - ed me.
But when I took Him at His word, For-giv'n He lift - ed me.
When from my guilt and grief, for-lorn, In love He lift - ed me.
Yet how or why, I can - not tell, He should have lift - ed me.
He lift - ed me.
CHORUS.
From sink-ing sand He lift - ed me, With ten - der hand He lift - ed me,
From shades of night to plains of light, O praise His name, He lift-ed me!

5. When They Ring the Golden Bells.

Dion De Marbelle.

M. 80 = ♩
1. There's a land be-yond the riv-er, That we call the sweet for-ev-er, And we
2. We shall know no sin nor sor-row, In that ha-ven of to-mor-row, When our
3. When our days shall know their number, When in death we sweet-ly slumber, When the
on-ly reach that shore by faith's decree; One by one we'll gain the portals, There to
barque shall sail beyond the sil-ver sea; We shall on-ly know the blessing Of our
King commands the spir-it to be free; Nev-er-more with anguish la-den, We shall
dwell with the immortals, When they ring the golden bells for you and me.
Father's sweet caressing, When they ring the golden bells for you and me.
reach that love-ly ai-den, When they ring the golden bells for you and me.
FINE.
you and me.
D.S.–yond the shining river, When they ring the golden bells for you and me.
CHORUS.
Don't you hear the bells now ringing? Don't you hear the an-gels sing-ing? 'Tis the
glo-ry hal-le-lu-jah Ju-bi-lee. (Ju-bi-lee.) In that far-off sweet forever, Just be-
D. S.

6 O That Will Be Glory.

C. H. G. Copyright, 1928, Renewal, Homer A. Rodeheaver, owner. Chas. H. Gabriel.

1. When all my la-bors and tri-als are o'er, And I am safe on that
2. When, by the gift of His in-fi-nite grace, I am ac-cord-ed in
3. Friends will be there I have loved long a-go; Joy like a ri- -er a-
beau-ti-ful shore, Just to be near the dear Lord I a-dore,
Heav-en a place, Just to be there and to look on His face,
round me will flow; Yet, just a smile from my Sav-ior, I know,
rit.
Will thro' the a-ges be glo-ry for me. . .
CHORUS. Faster.
O that will be
O . . . . that will
glo-ry for me, Glo-ry for me, glo-ry for me; When by His grace
be glo-ry for me, Glo-ry for me, glo-ry for me; . . . .
rit.
I shall look on His face, That will be glo-ry, be glo-ry for me.

I Walk With the King.

James Rowe. B. D. Ackley.

M. 80 — ♩.

1. In sor-row I wan-dered, my spir-it op-prest, But now I am
2. For years in the fet-ters of sin I was bound, The world could not
3. O soul near de-spair in the low-lands of strife, Look up and let

hap-py—se-cure-ly I rest; From morn-ing till eve-ning glad
help me—no com-fort I found; But now like the birds and the
Je-sus come in-to your life; The joy of sal-va-tion to

car-ols I sing, And this is the rea-son—I walk with the King.
sunbeams of Spring, I'm free and re-joic-ing—I walk with the King.
you He would bring—Come in-to the sun-light and walk with the King.

CHORUS.

I walk with the King, hal-le-lu-jah! I walk with the King, praise His name!
No long-er I roam, my soul fac-es home, I walk and I talk with the King.

Jesus, Rose of Sharon.

Ida A. Guirey. Chas. H. Gabriel.

M. 92 = ♩

1. Je - sus, Rose of Shar - on, bloom with-in my heart; Beau - ties of Thy
2. Je - sus, Rose of Shar - on, sweet - er far to see Than the fair - est
3. Je - sus, Rose of Shar - on, balm for ev - 'ry ill, May Thy ten - der
4. Je - sus, Rose of Shar - on, bloom for - ev - er-more; Be Thy glo - ry

truth and ho - li - ness im - part, That wher-e'er I go my life may
flow'rs of earth could ev - er be, Fill my life com-plete - ly, add - ing
mer - cies heal-ing pow'r dis - til For af - flict-ed souls of wea - ry,
seen on earth from shore to shore, Till the na-tions own Thy sov'reign-

shed a - broad Fra - grance of the knowledge of the love of God.
more each day Of Thy grace di - vine and pu - ri - ty, I pray.
bur - dened men, Giv - ing need - y mor-tals health and hope a - gain.
ty com-plete, Lay their hon - ors down and wor - ship at His feet.

CHORUS.

Je - sus,............. Rose of Shar - on,.............
Bless - ed Je - sus, Rose of Shar - on,

Bloom in ra - diance and in love with - in my heart.

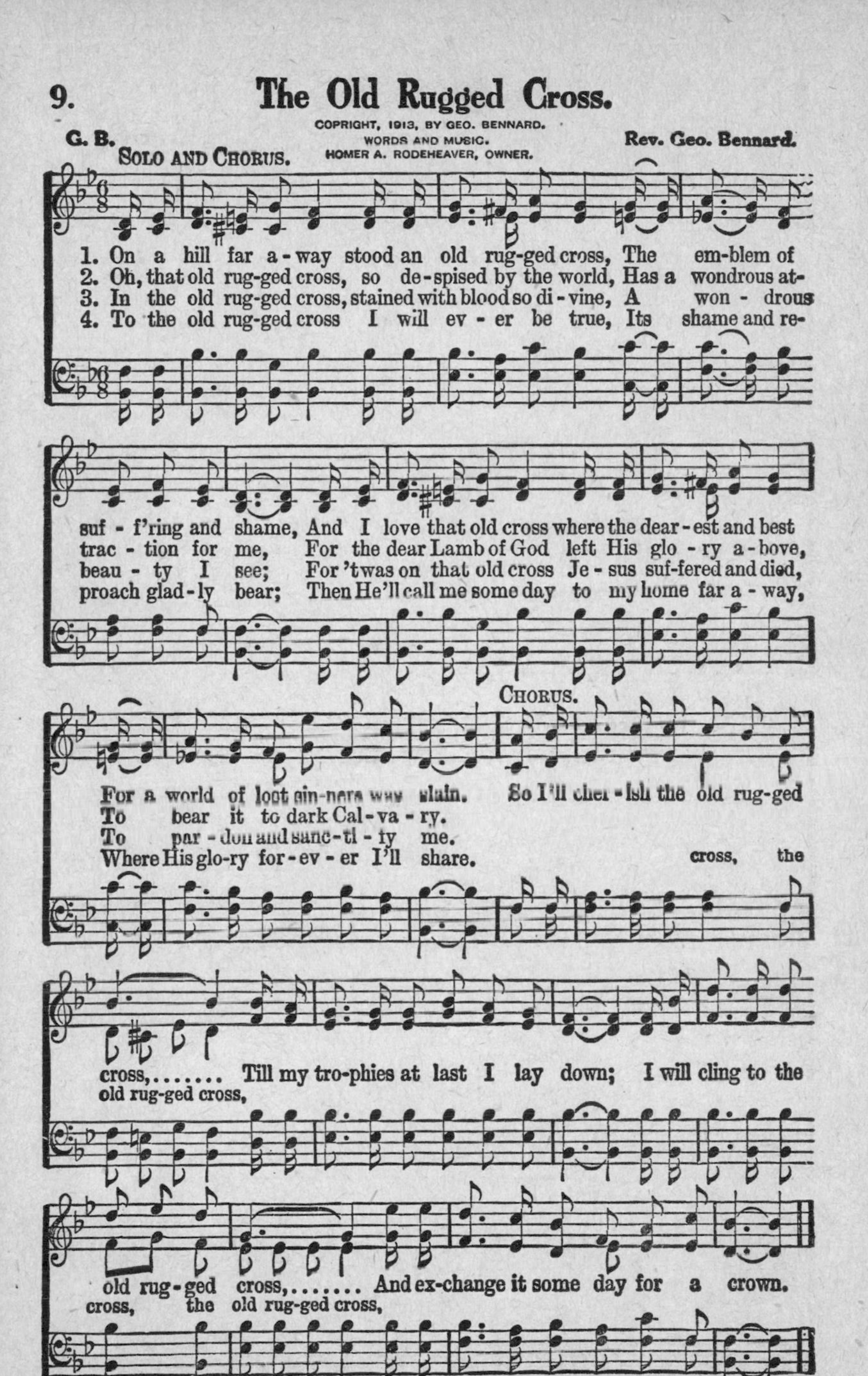
9.
The Old Rugged Cross.
COPRIGHT, 1913, BY GEO. BENNARD.
WORDS AND MUSIC.
HOMER A. RODEHEAVER, OWNER.
G. B.
Rev. Geo. Bennard.
SOLO AND CHORUS.
1. On a hill far a-way stood an old rug-ged cross, The em-blem of
2. Oh, that old rug-ged cross, so de-spised by the world, Has a wondrous at-
3. In the old rug-ged cross, stained with blood so di-vine, A won-drous
4. To the old rug-ged cross I will ev-er be true, Its shame and re-
suf-f'ring and shame, And I love that old cross where the dear-est and best
trac-tion for me, For the dear Lamb of God left His glo-ry a-bove,
beau-ty I see; For 'twas on that old cross Je-sus suf-fered and died,
proach glad-ly bear; Then He'll call me some day to my home far a-way,
For a world of lost sin-ners was slain.
To bear it to dark Cal-va-ry.
To par-don and sanc-ti-fy me.
Where His glo-ry for-ev-er I'll share.
CHORUS.
So I'll cher-ish the old rug-ged cross, the
cross,....... Till my tro-phies at last I lay down; I will cling to the
old rug-ged cross,
old rug-ged cross,....... And ex-change it some day for a crown.
cross, the old rug-ged cross,

10

The Hills Above.

R. M. Robert Matthews.

M. 126 = ♩
1. There are sun-lit hills a-bove me, And the hand of God is there, Where the valley shadows never reach And the sky is al-ways fair; Tho' my cares press heavy on me, And my heart is sore distressed, In the love of Christ my Savior I find perfect rest.
2. With the light of faith to guide me, And with hope at hand to cheer, I will struggle up the rugged steep, Never fal-ter, nev-er fear; I will leave the dismal val-ley, And a-bove the mists of sin, In the glo-ry of the sunlit hills New life be-gin.
3. When the shadows gather round me, And my sight is grow-ing dim, I will lift my eyes to heav'n above—For my help must come from Him. He will guide me thro' the valley, Where the path of life may wend, Till I reach the gates of glory And my journey's end.
CHORUS.
I will leave the misty val-ley for the sunlit hills a-bove, Yes, I'll leave the misty val-ley for the hills a-bove; God has led me from the shad-ow to the sun-light

The Hills Above.
of His love, So I'll leave the mist-y val - ley for the hills a - bove.
of His pre-cious love,
11.
More About Jesus.
E. E. Hewitt.
COPYRIGHT, 1887, BY JNO. R. SWENEY.
Jno. R. Sweney.
M. 63 = 𝅗𝅥.
1. More a-bout Je - sus I would know, More of His grace to oth-ers show;
2. More a-bout Je - sus let me learn, More of His ho - ly will dis-cern;
3. More a-bout Je - sus; in His word, Holding com-mun-ion with my Lord,
4. More a-bout Je - sus; on His throne, Rich-es in glo - ry all His own;
More of His sav - ing full-ness see, More of His love who died for me.
Spir - it of God, my teach-er be, Show-ing the things of Christ to me.
Hear-ing His voice in ev - 'ry line, Mak-ing each faith-ful say - ing mine.
More of His kingdom's sure increase; More of His com-ing, Prince of Peace.
Refrain.
More, more a-bout Je - sus, More, more a-bout Je - sus;
More of His sav-ing full-ness see, More of His love who died for me.

12. Since Jesus Came Into My Heart.

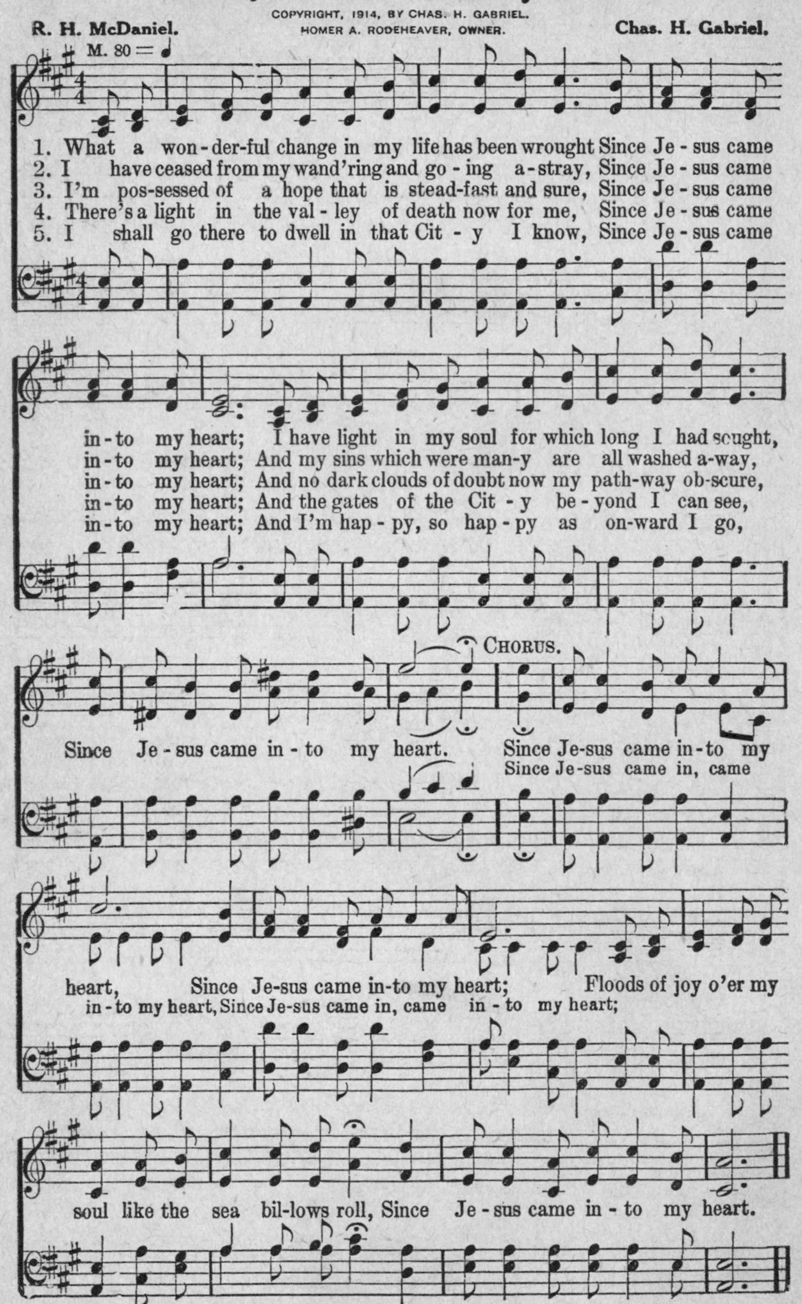
COPYRIGHT, 1914, BY CHAS. H. GABRIEL.
HOMER A. RODEHEAVER, OWNER.
R. H. McDaniel.
Chas. H. Gabriel.
M. 80 = ♩
1. What a won-der-ful change in my life has been wrought Since Je-sus came in-to my heart; I have light in my soul for which long I had sought, Since Je-sus came in-to my heart.
2. I have ceased from my wand'ring and go-ing a-stray, Since Je-sus came in-to my heart; And my sins which were man-y are all washed a-way,
3. I'm pos-sessed of a hope that is stead-fast and sure, Since Je-sus came in-to my heart; And no dark clouds of doubt now my path-way ob-scure,
4. There's a light in the val-ley of death now for me, Since Je-sus came in-to my heart; And the gates of the Cit-y be-yond I can see,
5. I shall go there to dwell in that Cit-y I know, Since Je-sus came in-to my heart; And I'm hap-py, so hap-py as on-ward I go,
CHORUS.
Since Je-sus came in-to my heart, Since Je-sus came in-to my heart;
Since Je-sus came in, came in-to my heart, Since Je-sus came in, came in-to my heart;
Floods of joy o'er my soul like the sea bil-lows roll, Since Je-sus came in-to my heart.

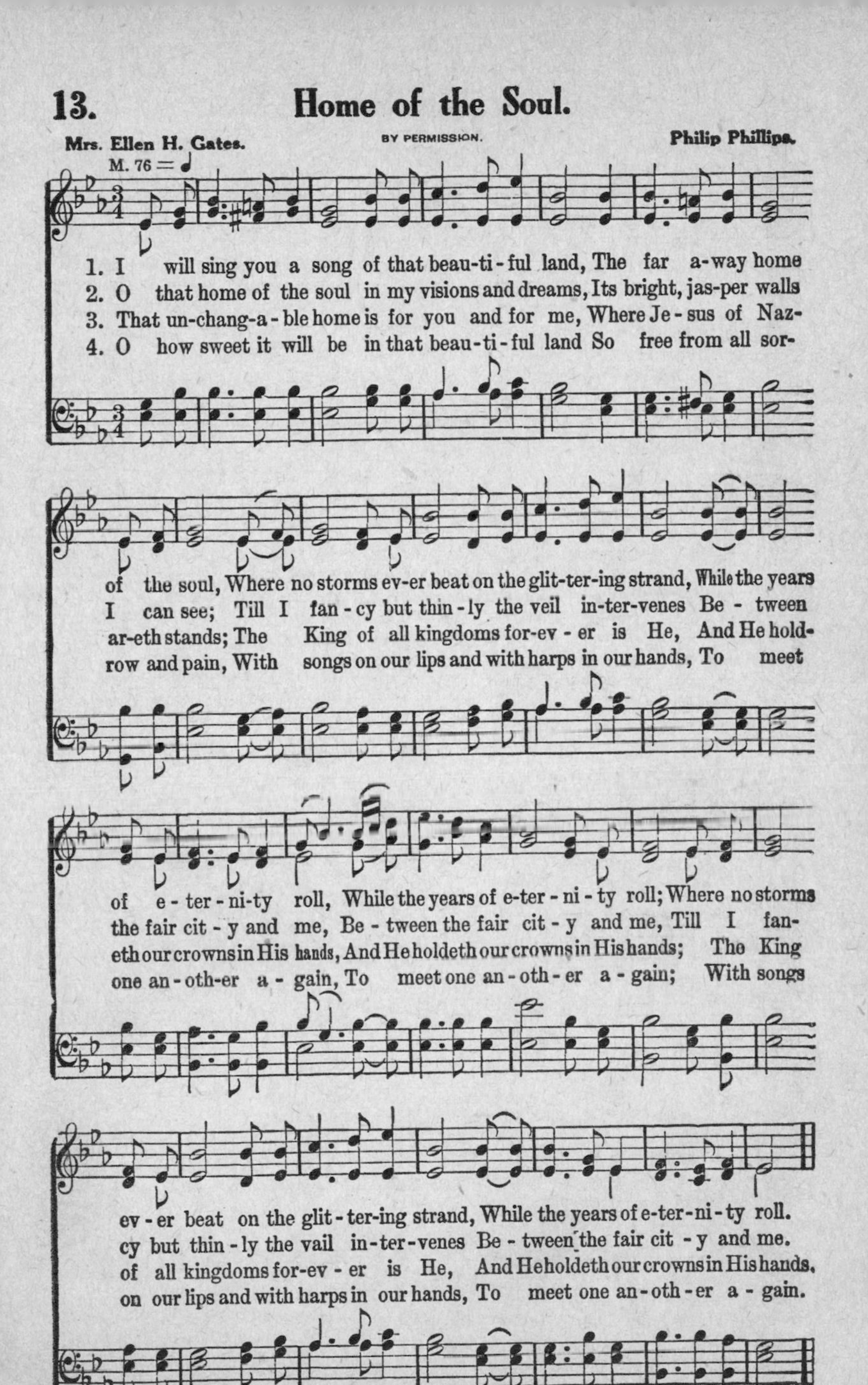
13.
Home of the Soul.
Mrs. Ellen H. Gates.
BY PERMISSION.
Philip Phillips.
M. 76 = ♩
1. I will sing you a song of that beau-ti-ful land, The far a-way home
2. O that home of the soul in my visions and dreams, Its bright, jas-per walls
3. That un-chang-a-ble home is for you and for me, Where Je-sus of Naz-
4. O how sweet it will be in that beau-ti-ful land So free from all sor-
of the soul, Where no storms ev-er beat on the glit-ter-ing strand, While the years
I can see; Till I fan-cy but thin-ly the veil in-ter-venes Be - tween
ar-eth stands; The King of all kingdoms for-ev - er is He, And He hold-
row and pain, With songs on our lips and with harps in our hands, To meet
of e-ter-ni-ty roll, While the years of e-ter-ni-ty roll; Where no storms
the fair cit-y and me, Be-tween the fair cit-y and me, Till I fan-
eth our crowns in His hands, And He holdeth our crowns in His hands; The King
one an-oth-er a-gain, To meet one an-oth-er a-gain; With songs
ev-er beat on the glit-ter-ing strand, While the years of e-ter-ni-ty roll.
cy but thin-ly the vail in-ter-venes Be-tween the fair cit-y and me.
of all kingdoms for-ev-er is He, And He holdeth our crowns in His hands.
on our lips and with harps in our hands, To meet one an-oth-er a-gain.

14. I Have a Savior.

COPYRIGHT, 1922, BY HOMER A. RODEHEAVER.
INTERNATIONAL COPYRIGHT SECURED.
W. C. Poole.
J. M. Hagan.
M. 63=
1. I have a Sav - ior who light-ens my way, I have a Sav - ior who brightens the day, I have a Sav - ior who hears when I pray,— 'Tis Je - sus, the Light of the world.
2. I have a Sav - ior who al-ways is true, I have a Sav - ior who al - ways will do All He has prom-ised for me and for you,— 'Tis
3. I have a Sav - ior wher - ev - er I be, I have a Sav - ior on land or on sea, Car-ing and watch-ing in love o - ver me,— 'Tis
4. I have a Sav - ior who's reigning with - in, Read-y and anx - ious to help me to win Vic - to - ry o - ver all e - vil and sin,— 'Tis
CHORUS.
He makes my way light-er, He makes my day brighter, He walks all life's journey with me; with me; His pres-ence and glo - ry are round me and o'er me, And light-ens the path-way for me.

15.
Confidence.
E. B. Barnes.
COPYRIGHT, 1911, BY HOMER A. RODEHEAVER.
Homer A. Rodeheaver.
M. 66 = ♩
1. Walk Thou with me, nor let my foot-steps stray A - part from Thee, thro'-
2. Thro' wea - ry years my way hath mi - ry been; My bit - ter tears Thy
3. No earth - ly foe can give my spir - it fear; No threat'ning woe can
out life's threat'ning way; Be Thou my guide! the path I can - not see; Close to Thy
pity - ing eye hath seen; My fainting heart hath heard Thy voice divine; My trembling
quail when Thou art near; No tempter's snare can turn my steps a-side, For, in Thy
CHORUS.
side, Lord, let me walk with Thee.
hand asks but to rest in Thine. Dear Sav-ior, let me trust my hand in Thine,
care, I'm safe what-e'er be - tide.
And let me know Thy steps are guid - ing mine; Life's changing way is
rall.
oft-times dark to me; I fear no ill if I may walk with Thee.

16. # A Wonderful Savior.

Rev. R. H. McDaniel.

Chas. H. Gabriel.

M. 69 = 𝅗𝅥.
1. I am hap-py in Je-sus as home-ward I go; With His love and sal-
2. He is near to sus-tain me, to keep and to guide; There is nev-er an
3. He's a foun-tain of joy to my soul ev-'ry day, For He driv-eth my
4. And when I get home in His pres-ence to dwell, I will join heav-en's
va-tion my heart is a-glow, And I'm tell-ing the world that He
hour but He's close to my side, And to Him all my troub-les and
dark-ness and sor-rows a-way, And the joy that He gives me will
cho-rus His prais-es to swell, And for-ev-er and ev-er this
saves me, I know; He's a won-der-ful, won-der-ful Sav-ior to me.
cares I con-fide; He's a won-der-ful, won-der-ful Sav-ior to me.
nev-er de-cay; He's a won-der-ful, won-der-ful Sav-ior to me.
sto-ry I'll tell: He's a won-der-ful, won-der-ful Sav-ior to me.
CHORUS.
He's a won-der-ful Sav-ior, a won-der-ful Sav-ior, A
won-der-ful Sav-ior to me! .... I'll sing of His
won-der-ful Sav-ior to me!

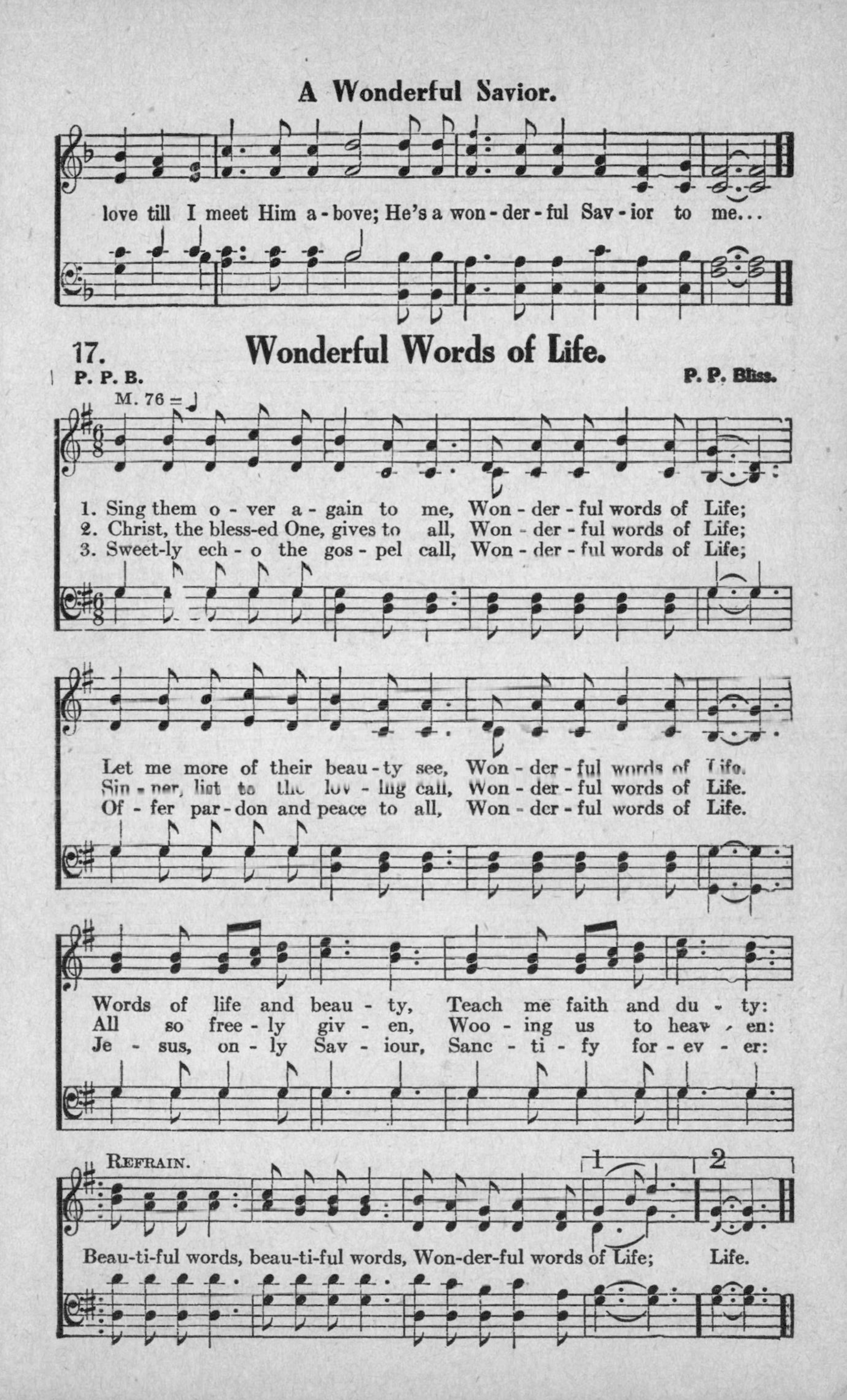
A Wonderful Savior.
love till I meet Him a-bove; He's a won-der-ful Sav-ior to me...
17.
Wonderful Words of Life.
P. P. B.
P. P. Bliss.
M. 76 = ♩
1. Sing them o-ver a-gain to me, Won-der-ful words of Life;
2. Christ, the bless-ed One, gives to all, Won-der-ful words of Life;
3. Sweet-ly ech-o the gos-pel call, Won-der-ful words of Life;
Let me more of their beau-ty see, Won-der-ful words of Life.
Sin-ner, list to the lov-ing call, Won-der-ful words of Life.
Of-fer par-don and peace to all, Won-der-ful words of Life.
Words of life and beau-ty, Teach me faith and du-ty:
All so free-ly giv-en, Woo-ing us to heav-en:
Je-sus, on-ly Sav-iour, Sanc-ti-fy for-ev-er:
Refrain.
1
2
Beau-ti-ful words, beau-ti-ful words, Won-der-ful words of Life; Life.

18.
He Whispers His Love to Me.
V. McC.
COPYRIGHT, 1920, BY HOMER A. RODEHEAVER.
INTERNATIONAL COPYRIGHT SECURED.
Vivian McCown.
M. 104 = ♩
1. 'Tis so sweet just to know that a - long the way Je - sus walks by my
2. When He scat-ters the gifts from His boundless store, And His show-ers of
3. When my heart is so tempt-ed and sore - ly tried, It is then that I
4. Oh, His voice is so won-drous-ly sweet to me! There's no mu-sic on
side all the live - long day, And He knows when the shad - ows be-
bless-ing a - round me pour, Lest I hum - ble and grate-ful for-
know He is by my side, And I know He will give me the
earth has such mel - o - dy; There's no joy that can come to the
gin to low'r, And He whis-pers His love to me o'er and o'er.
get to be, Je - sus whis-pers His won - der - ful love to me.
vic - to - ry As He whis-pers His won - der - ful love to me.
hu - man heart Like the joy that His love ev - er doth im - part.
CHORUS.
He whispers His love to me, He whispers His love to me;
His love to me, His love to me;
Lest I should stray from Him a - way, He whis-pers His love to me.

19. **My Wonderful Dream.**

Jessie Brown Pounds. Chas. H. Gabriel.

M. 44 = ♩.

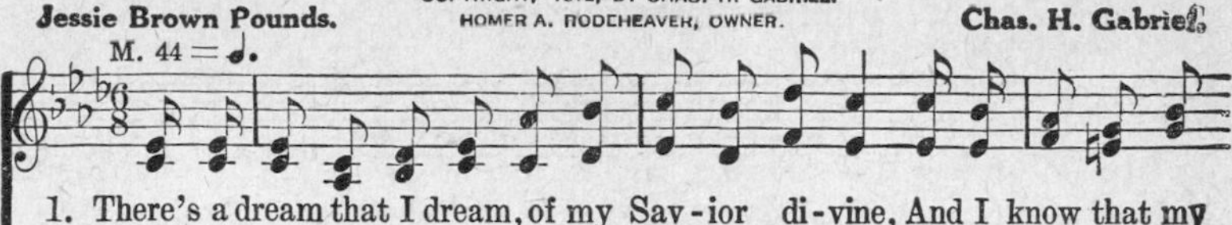

1. There's a dream that I dream, of my Sav - ior di - vine, And I know that my
2. There is sweet com-pen-sa-tion for heart-ache and loss In the hope that is
3. It will still be my stay when the fashion's of earth In the mist are dis-

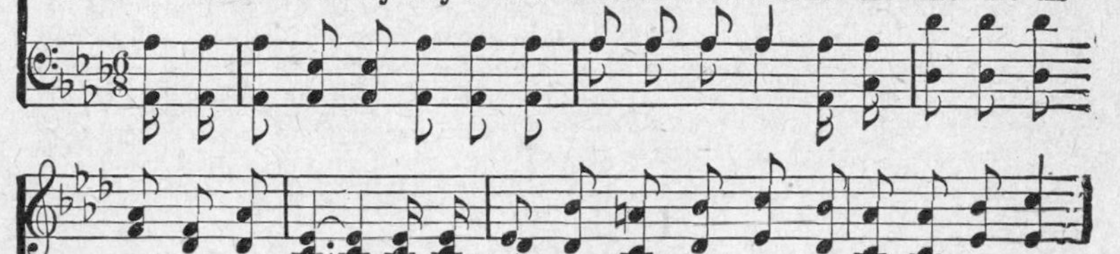

dream will come true; At the morn, in the night, comes the vis - ion of light,
giv - en to me; I shall quick-ly for - get how the road was be - set,
solv - ing a - way; For the pas - sage of death will be on - ly a breath

CHORUS.

With a prom-ise e - ter - nal - ly new.
When the King in His beau - ty I see. O this won-der-ful dream is a
But a breath, and my dream will come true.

se - cret of grace, And I would that this se - cret you knew;...... For I
that you knew;

dream that at last I shall look on His face, And I know that my dream will come true.

20. Sweeter As the Years Go By.

Mrs. C. H. M. | Mrs. C. H. Morris.

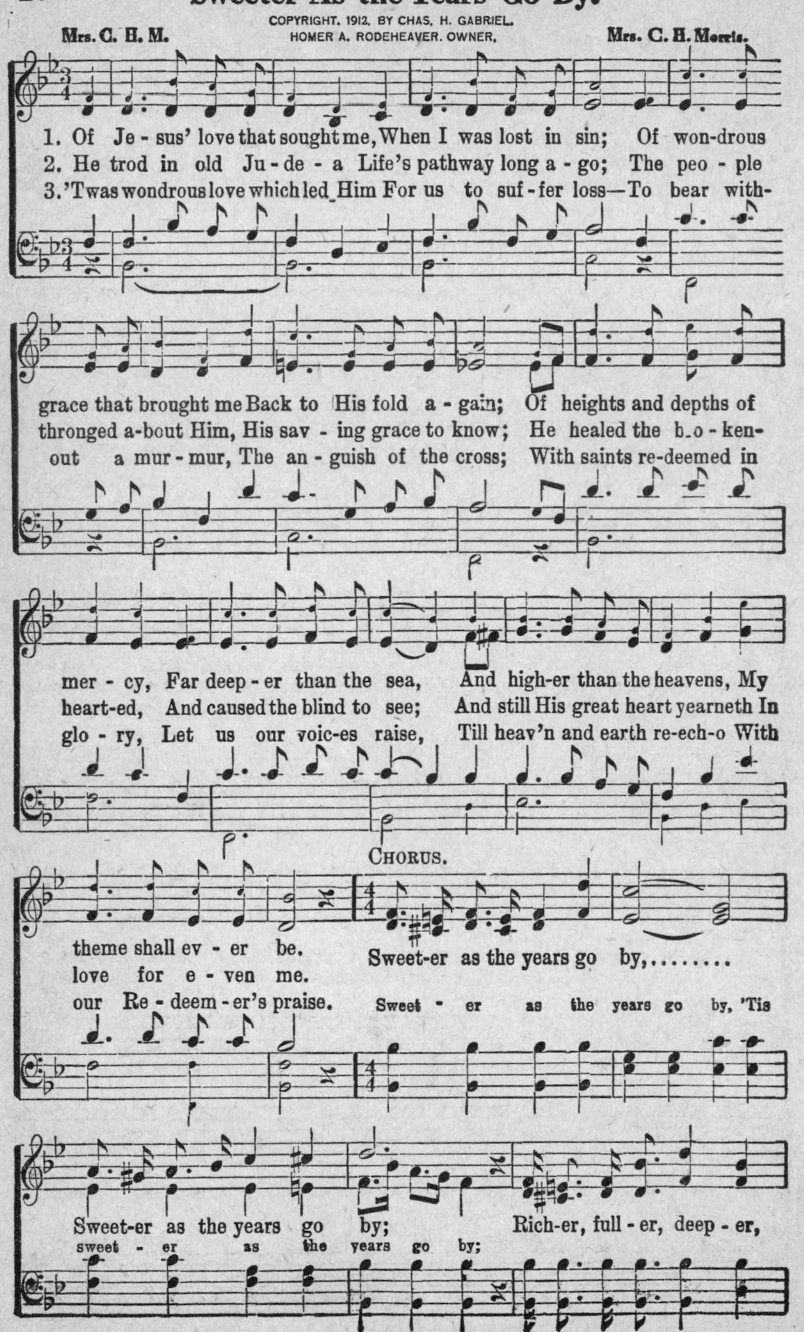
1. Of Je - sus' love that sought me, When I was lost in sin; Of won-drous
2. He trod in old Ju - de - a Life's pathway long a - go; The peo - ple
3. 'Twas wondrous love which led Him For us to suf - fer loss—To bear with-
grace that brought me Back to His fold a - gain; Of heights and depths of
thronged a-bout Him, His sav - ing grace to know; He healed the b_o - ken-
out a mur - mur, The an - guish of the cross; With saints re-deemed in
mer - cy, Far deep - er than the sea, And high-er than the heavens, My
heart-ed, And caused the blind to see; And still His great heart yearneth In
glo - ry, Let us our voic-es raise, Till heav'n and earth re-ech-o With
theme shall ev - er be.
love for e - ven me.
our Re - deem - er's praise.
CHORUS.
Sweet-er as the years go by,........
Sweet - er as the years go by, 'Tis
Sweet-er as the years go by;
sweet - er as the years go by;
Rich-er, full - er, deep - er,

Sweeter As the Years Go By.
rit.
Je - sus' love is sweet - er, Sweet - er as the years go by.
21.
The King At the Door.
COPYRIGHT, 1922, BY HOMER A. RODEHEAVER.
INTERNATIONAL COPYRIGHT SECURED.
L. S. L.
Lida Shivers Leech.
DUET.
M. 60 = ♩.
1. A Friend who's knocking at thy heart's door, A Friend who oft - en has
2. He knocks so gen - tly with nail-pierced hand; Ah, who His plead - ing could
3. The King of glo - ry now waits out - side, My heart's closed door I will
rit.
knocked before; He waits so pa-tient-ly just out-side: It is Christ the Lord.
long withstand! Blest Son of God, mighty Friend of man, Stands at thy heart's door.
o - pen wide; Come in, dear Savior, and e'er a-bide, Be my all in all.
REFRAIN.
'Tis the King at the door, let Him in,.... He will cleanse you from guilt and from
door,.......let Him in,
guilt, from
sin;.... Oh, the matchless love of the King above, To be stand-ing there!
guilt and sin;

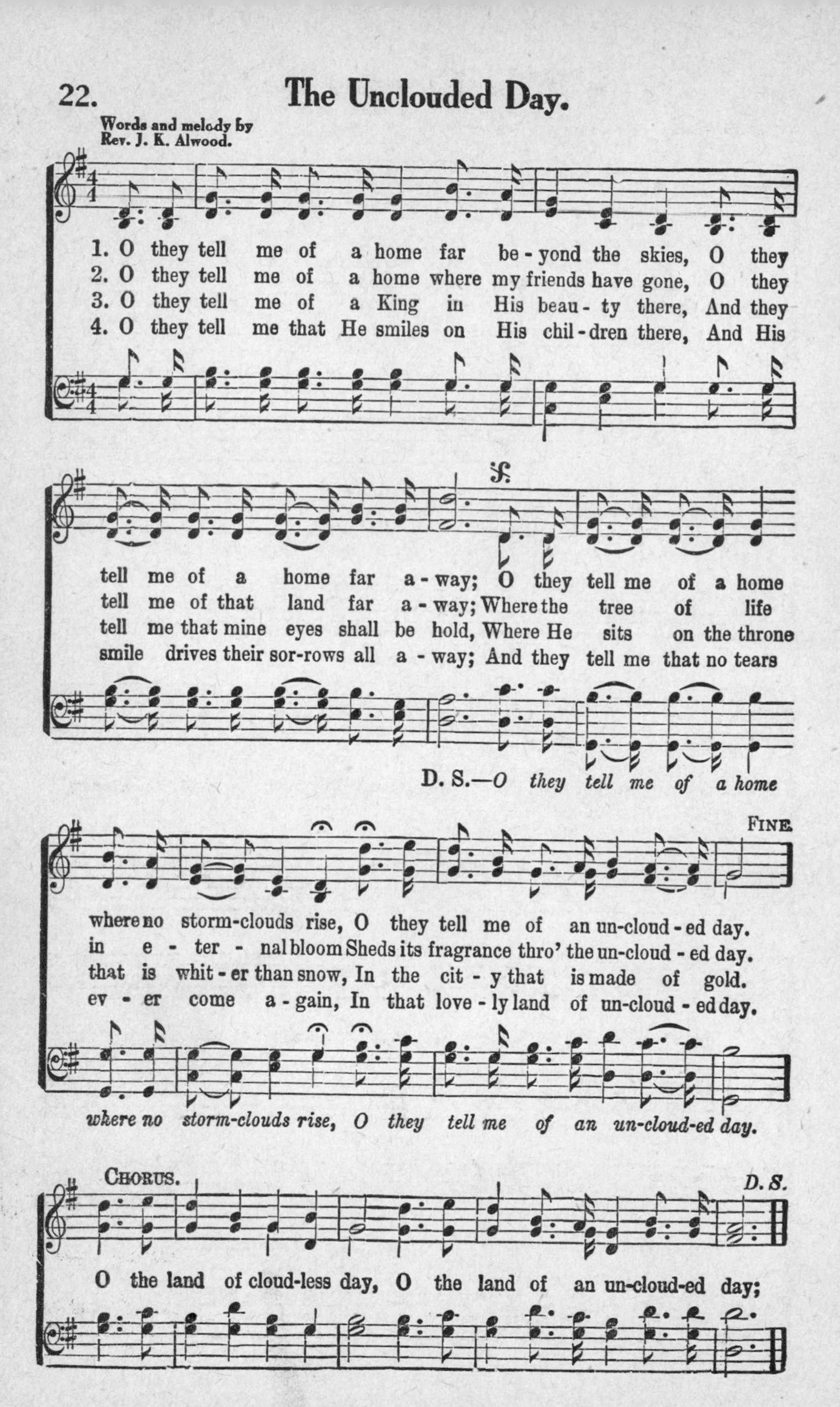
22.
The Unclouded Day.
Words and melody by
Rev. J. K. Alwood.
1. O they tell me of a home far be - yond the skies, O they tell me of a home far a - way; O they tell me of a home where no storm-clouds rise, O they tell me of an un-cloud - ed day.
2. O they tell me of a home where my friends have gone, O they tell me of that land far a - way; Where the tree of life in e - ter - nal bloom Sheds its fragrance thro' the un-cloud - ed day.
3. O they tell me of a King in His beau - ty there, And they tell me that mine eyes shall be hold, Where He sits on the throne that is whit - er than snow, In the cit - y that is made of gold.
4. O they tell me that He smiles on His chil - dren there, And His smile drives their sor-rows all a - way; And they tell me that no tears ev - er come a - gain, In that love - ly land of un-cloud - ed day.
D. S.—O they tell me of a home where no storm-clouds rise, O they tell me of an un-cloud-ed day.
FINE
CHORUS.
O the land of cloud-less day, O the land of an un-cloud-ed day;
D. S.

23. Is It the Crowning Day?

George Walker Whitcomb. Charles H. Marsh.

M. 63
1. Je - sus may come to - day, Glad day, Glad day! And I would
2. I may go home to - day, Glad day, Glad day! Seem-eth I
3. Why should I anx - ious be? Glad day, Glad day! Lights ap-pear
4. Faith-ful I'll be to - day, Glad day, Glad day! And I will
see my Friend; Dan - gers and troub - les would end If
hear their song; Hail to the ra - di - ant throng! If
on the shore, Storms will af - fright nev - er - more, For
free - ly tell Why I should love Him so well, For
CHORUS.
Je-sus should come to-day.
I should go home to-day.
He is "at hand" to-day.
He is my all to-day.
Glad day, Glad day! Is it the crown - ing
day? I'll live for to-day, nor anx - ious be; Je-sus my Lord I
rit.
soon shall see. Glad day, Glad day! Is it the crown-ing day?

24.
In The Garden.
C. A. M.
COPYRIGHT. 1912, BY HALL-MACK CO.
INTERNATIONAL COPYRIGHT SECURED.
C. Austin Miles.
1. I come to the gar-den a-lone, While the dew is still on the
2. He speaks, and the sound of His voice Is so sweet the birds hush their
3. I'd stay in the gar-den with Him Tho' the night a-round me be
ros-es; And the voice I hear, Fall-ing on my ear; The
sing-ing, And the mel-o-dy That He gave to me, With-
fall-ing, But He bids me go; Thro' the voice of woe, His
Son of God dis-clos-es.
in my heart is ring-ing.
voice to me is call-ing.
CHORUS.
And He walks with me, and He
talks with me, And He tells me I am His own, And the
joy we share as we tar-ry there, None oth-er has ev-er known.

25. Where the Gates Swing Outward Never.

C. H. G. Chas. H. Gabriel.

M. 92 =
1. Just a few more days to be filled with praise, And to tell the
2. Just a few more years with their toil and tears, And the jour-ney
3. Tho' the hills be steep and the val-leys deep, With no flow'rs my
4. What a joy 'twill be when I wake to see Him for whom my
old, old sto-ry; Then, when twi-light falls, and my Sav-ior calls,
will be end-ed; Then I'll be with Him, where the tide of time
way a-dorn-ing; Tho' the night be lone and my rest a stone,
heart is burn-ing! Nev-er-more to sigh, nev-er-more to die—
CHORUS.
I shall go to Him in glo-ry.
With e-ter-ni-ty is blend-ed. I'll ex change my cross for a
Joy a-waits me in the morn-ing.
For that day my heart is yearn-ing.
star-ry crown, Where the gates swing outward nev-er; At His feet I'll
lay ev-'ry bur-den down, And with Je-sus reign for-ev-er.

26.

Love Found a Way.

Avis M. Christianson. Chas. H. Gabriel.

M. 63 = 𝅗𝅥.
1. I was a sin-ner! no hope could I see Till, in His mer-cy so won-drous and free, Je-sus looked down in com-pas-sion on me, And
2. Darkness and sin had en-vel-oped my soul; I was com-plete-ly in Sa-tan's con-trol, But, bless the Lord, Christ in love made me whole—And
3. Nev-er shall sin rule with-in me a-gain; Je-sus has cleansed ev-'ry blem-ish and stain; King of all kings He for-ev-er shall reign, For
CHORUS.
Love found the way to my heart! Love found the way to my heart!
Love found the way, the way to my heart!
Love found the way to my heart! Dark-ness was 'round me, For
Love found the way, the way to my heart!
Sa-tan had bound me, Yet Love found the way to my heart!

27 The End of the Road.

Dedicated to Evangelist Harry W. Vom Bruck

COPYRIGHT, 1920, BY ELTON M. ROTH.
HOMER A. RODEHEAVER, OWNER.
Lizzie DeArmond.
Elton M. Roth.
M. 108 = ♩
1. When I come to the end of the long, long road, The shad-ows will flee a - way,
will flee a - way,
And I'll stand in the glo - ri-ous light of God, Where dwell-eth e - ter - nal day.......
2. Looking back o'er the years that were hard and drear, The hand of the Christ I'll see;
the Christ I'll see;
While my heart will go forth with a song of praise, Be - cause of His love for me.......
3. When I come to the end of the long, long road, And tri - als will all be past,
will all be past,
I shall look in the face of my dear-est Friend, Safe home in His heav'n at last.......
CHORUS.
When I come to the end, the end of the road, To the land of e - ter - ni - ty,
When I come to the
To the land of e - ter - ni - ty,
When I come to the end of life's long road, The face of my Lord I'll see.
rit.

28. Good Night and Good Morning.

Lizzie DeArmond. Homer A. Rodeheaver.

M. 85 = ♩
1. When comes to the wea - ry a bless - ed re - lease, When up-ward we
2. When fad - eth the day and dark shad-ows draw nigh, With Christ close at
3. When home-lights we see shin - ing bright - ly a - bove, Where we shall be
pass to His king-dom of peace, When free from the woes that on earth we must bear,
hand, it is not death to die; He'll wipe ev-'ry tear, roll a - way ev-'ry care;
soon, thro' His won-der-ful love, We'll praise Him who called us His heav-en to share,
CHORUS.
We'll say "good-night," here, but "good-morn - ing" up there.
We'll say "good-night," here, but "good-morn - ing" up there. Good-morn-ing up there where
We'll say "good-night," here, but "good-morn - ing" up there.
Christ is the Light, Good-morn - ing up there where cometh no night; When we step from this
earth to God's heaven so fair, We'll say "good-night" here, but "good-morn-ing" up there.

29. Tell Me the Story of Jesus.

Fanny J. Crosby. Jno. R. Sweney.

M. 100 = ♩

1. Tell me the sto - ry of Je - sus, Write on my heart ev - 'ry word;
2. Fast-ing a-lone in the des - ert, Tell of the days that are passed,
3. Tell of the cross where they nailed Him, Writh-ing in an-guish and pain;

CHO.—*Tell me the sto - ry of Je - sus, Write on my heart ev - 'ry word;*

FINE.

Tell me the sto - ry most pre - cious, Sweet-est that ev - er was heard.
How for our sins He was tempt - ed, Yet was tri-um-phant at last.
Tell of the grave where they laid Him, Tell how He liv - eth a - gain.

Tell me the sto - ry most pre-cious, Sweet-est that ev - er was heard.

Tell how the an - gels, in cho - rus, Sang as they wel-comed His birth,
Tell of the years of His la - bor, Tell of the sor - row He bore,
Love in that sto - ry so ten - der, Clear - er than ev - er I see;

D.C. for Cho.

"Glo - ry to God in the high - est! Peace and good ti - dings to earth."
He was de-spised and af - flict - ed, Home-less, re - ject-ed and poor.
Stay, let me weep while you whis - per, Love paid the ran-som for me.

30. Where They Never Say "Good-bye."

COPYRIGHT, 1922, BY HOMER A. RODEHEAVER.
INTERNATIONAL COPYRIGHT SECURED
Rev. A. H. Ackley.
B. D. Ackley.
M. 92 = ♩ SOLO.—Do not hurry.
1. There's a land where the birds are ev - er sing - ing, Where the flow'rs in their
2. We shall tell of the way that we have trav-eled, When at last we shall
3. We shall gaze on His face in ad - o - ra - tion, Joy re-splen-dent shall
beau-ty nev-er fade, Where the joy-bells of love are ev - er ring - ing,
en - ter heav-en's door, And the prob-lems of life will be un - rav - eled,
thrill our souls a - new, As we crown Him the King of our sal - va - tion,
And no e - vil shall ev - er dare in - vade.
When we meet on that bright e - ter - nal shore.
And e - ter - ni - ty's glo - ries come to view.
CHORUS.
In the land where they
nev - er say good-bye,
No sad part - ings, for none shall ev - er
rall.
die; (shall ev - er die;) We shall sing the same old sto - ry, We shall

Where They Never Say "Good-bye."
wear a crown of glo-ry, In the land where they nev-er say good-bye..........
they nev-er say good-bye.
31 'Tis So Sweet to Trust in Jesus.
Mrs. Louisa M. R. Stead. Copyright, 1882, by Wm. J. Kirkpatrick. Wm. J. Kirkpatrick.
M. 92 = ♩
1. 'Tis so sweet to trust in Je - sus, Just to take Him at His word;
2. Oh, how sweet to trust in Je - sus, Just to trust His cleansing blood;
3. Yes, 'tis sweet to trust in Je - sus, Just from sin and self to cease;
4. I'm so glad I learn'd to trust Thee, Pre-cious Je - sus, Savior, Friend;
Just to rest up - on His prom-ise; Just to know "Thus saith the Lord."
Just in sim - ple faith to plunge me 'Neath the heal-ing, cleans-ing flood.
Just from Je - sus sim - ply tak - ing Life and rest, and joy and peace.
And I know that Thou art with me, Wilt be with me to the end.
CHORUS.
Je - sus, Je - sus, how I trust Him! How I've proved Him o'er and o'er!
p
Je - sus, Je - sus, pre-cious Je - sus! O for grace to trust Him more.

32. O Love That Will Not Let Me Go.

Rev. Geo. Matheson.
COPYRIGHT, 1910, BY HOMER A. RODEHEAVER.
J. B. Herbert.
May be sung as duet, Soprano and Tenor.
M. 76 =
1. O love that will not let me go, I rest my
2. O light that fol-lowest all my way I yield my
3. O joy that seek-est me thro' pain, I can-not
4. O cross that lift-est up my head, I dare not
wea-ry soul in Thee; I give Thee back the life I
flick-'ring torch to Thee; My heart re-stores its bor-rowed
close my heart to Thee; I trace the rain-bow thro' the
ask to fly from Thee; I lay in dust life's glo-ry
owe, That in Thine o-cean depths its flow May
ray, That in Thy sun-shine's blaze its day May
rain, And feel the prom-ise is not vain That
dead, And from the ground there blos-soms red Life
rich-er, full-er be, May rich-er, full-er be.
bright-er, fair-er be, May bright-er, fair-er be.
morn shall tear-less be, That morn shall tear-less be.
that shall end-less be, Life that shall end-less be.

33. Take Up Thy Cross.

A. H. A. — Rev. A. H. Ackley.

Slowly with expression. M. 88 = ♩
1. I walked one day a - long a coun-try road, And there a stranger journeyed, too,
2. I cried, "Lord Jesus," and He spoke my name; I saw His hands all bruised and torn;
3. "O let me bear Thy cross, dear Lord," I cried, And, lo, a cross for me appeared,
4. My cross I'll car-ry till the crown ap-pears, The way I jour-ney soon will end
Bent low be-neath the burden of His load: It was a cross, a cross I knew.
I stooped to kiss a-way the marks of shame, The shame for me that He had borne.
The one for-got-ten, I had cast a - side, The one, so long, that I had feared.
Where God Himself shall wipe away all tears, And friend hold fellowship with friend.
CHORUS.
"Take up thy cross and follow Me," I hear the blessed Sav-ior call;
How can I make a less-er sac - ri - fice, When Je - sus gave His all?

34. The Border Land.

R. M.
Robeet Matthews.
1. Are you on the Bor-der Land? On the Bor - der Land? Do you hes - i - ta - ting stand On the Bor - der Land? Take the step, do not de - lay, You are drift - ing far a-way, Far a - way from the Bor - der Land.
2. Is it sin that holds you back, On the Bor - der Land? Is it cour - age that you lack On the Bor - der Land? Look to Je - sus while you may, He will give you strength to-day, Strength to cross from the Bor - der Land.
3. You can hear His pleading voice, On the Bor - der Land; Come to Me and make your choice, On the Bor - der Land; Con - se - crate your life to me, And your guide and friend I'll be, Sav-iour, Friend, o'er the Bor - der Land.
Chorus.
On the Border Land, on the Bor-der Land; O my friend, you can no long-er stand,
cres.
Heark-en to the call, Hear the Lord's command, Sinner, come across the Bor-der Land.
BY PERMISSION OF R. MATTHEWS, OWNER.

35. I'm a Pilgrim.

COPYRIGHT, 1911, BY RODEHEAVER & HERBERT.
HOMER A RODEHEAVER. OWNER.
Mary S. B. Dana.
J. B. Herbert.
Duet.
1. I'm a pil-grim, and I'm a stran - ger, I can tar - ry, I can
2. Of that cit - y to which I jour - ney, My Re - deem-er, my Re-
3. There the sun-beams are ev - er shin - ing, O my long-ing heart, my
tar - ry but a night! Do not de - tain me, for I am go - ing,
deem-er is the Light; There is no sor - row, nor an - y sigh - ing,
long-ing heart is there; Here in this coun - try, so dark and drear - y
Chorus.
To where the fountains are ev - er flow - ing.
Nor an - y tears there, nor an - y dy - ing. I'm a pil-grim, and I'm a
I long have wandered for-lorn and wea - ry.
stran - ger, I can tar - ry, I can tar - ry but a night! I'm a
pil-grim, and I'm a stran-ger, I can tar - ry, I can tar - ry but a night!

Transformed.

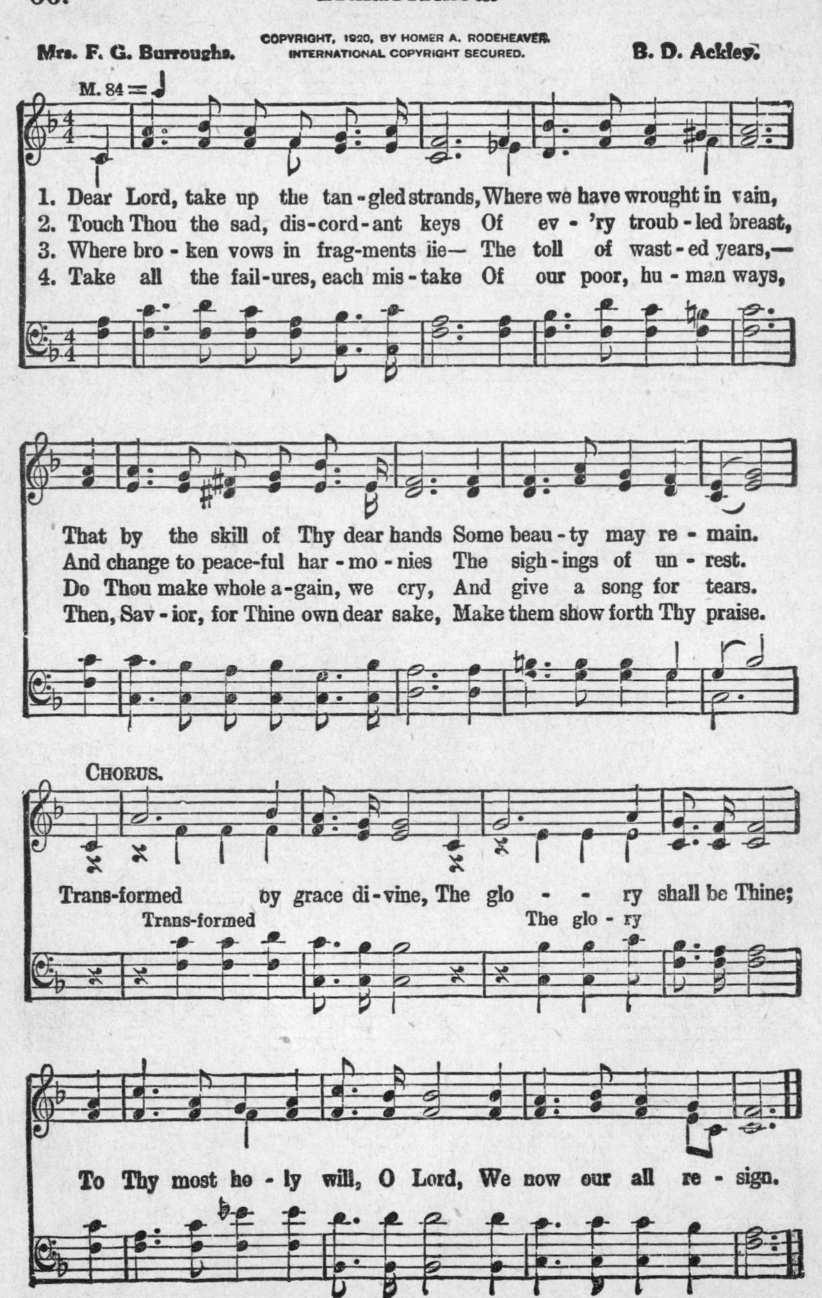
Mrs. F. G. Burroughs.
COPYRIGHT, 1920, BY HOMER A. RODEHEAVER.
INTERNATIONAL COPYRIGHT SECURED.
B. D. Ackley.
M. 84
1. Dear Lord, take up the tan-gled strands, Where we have wrought in vain,
2. Touch Thou the sad, dis-cord-ant keys Of ev-'ry troub-led breast,
3. Where bro-ken vows in frag-ments lie— The toll of wast-ed years,—
4. Take all the fail-ures, each mis-take Of our poor, hu-man ways,
That by the skill of Thy dear hands Some beau-ty may re-main.
And change to peace-ful har-mo-nies The sigh-ings of un-rest.
Do Thou make whole a-gain, we cry, And give a song for tears.
Then, Sav-ior, for Thine own dear sake, Make them show forth Thy praise.
CHORUS.
Trans-formed by grace di-vine, The glo-ry shall be Thine;
Trans-formed
The glo-ry
To Thy most ho-ly will, O Lord, We now our all re-sign.

37. Beulah Land.

Edgar Page. BY PERMISSION OF MRS L. E. SWENEY KIRKPATRICK. Jno. R. Sweney.

M. 80 = ♩
1. I've reached the land of corn and wine, And all its rich - es free - ly mine;
2. My Sav-ior comes and walks with me, And sweet com-mun-ion here have we;
3. A sweet per-fume up - on the breeze Is born from ev - er - ver - nal trees,
4. The zeph-yrs seem to float to me, Sweet sounds of heav-en's mel - o - dy,
Here shines undimmed one bliss - ful day, For all my night has passed a-way.
He gen - tly leads me by His hand, For this is heav-en's bor - der-land.
And flow'rs, that nev - er - fad - ing grow Where streams of life for - ev - er flow.
As an-gels with the white-robed throng Join in the sweet redemption song.
CHORUS.
O Beu-lah Land, sweet Beu-lah Land, As on thy high-est mount I stand,
I look a-way a- cross the sea, Where mansions are pre-pared for me,
And view the shin - ing glo-ry-shore— My heav'n, my home for-ev - er-more!

My Savior First of All.

Fanny J. Crosby. — Jno. R. Sweney.

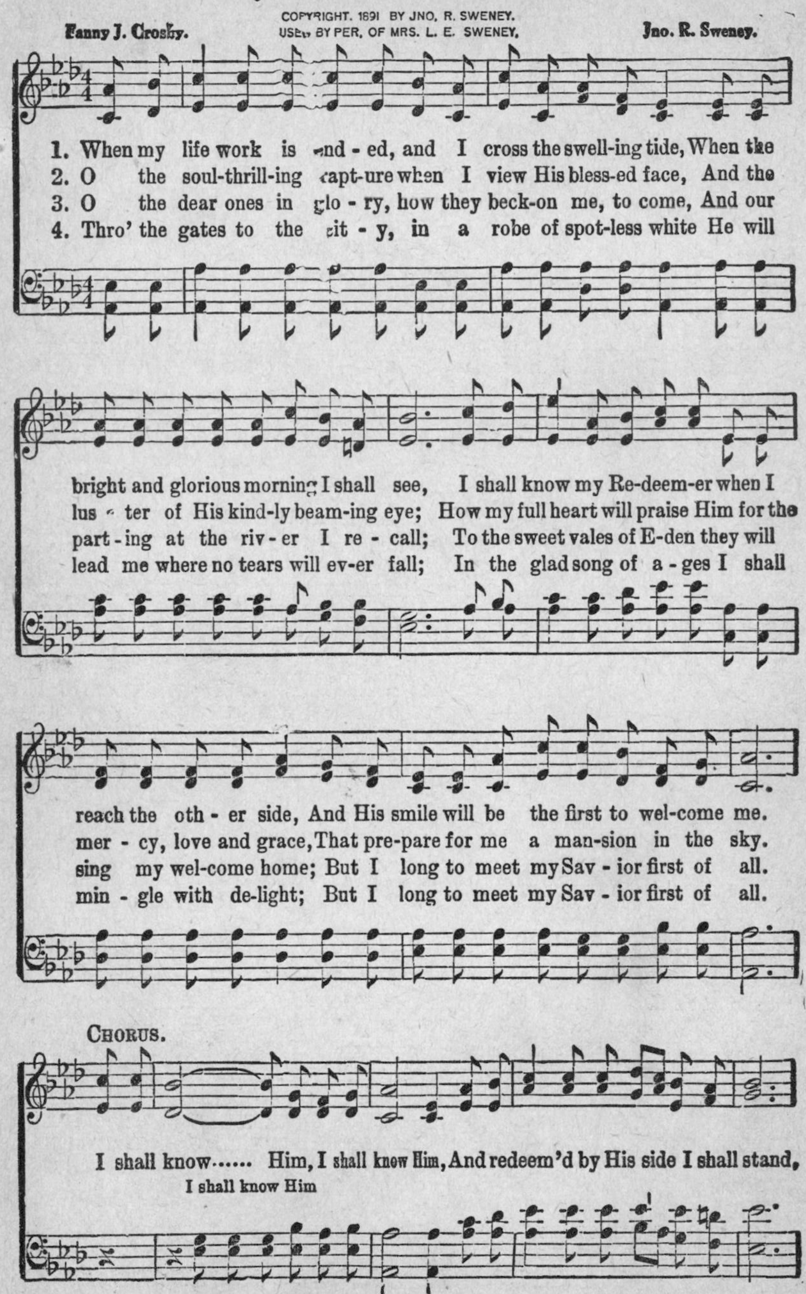
1. When my life work is end - ed, and I cross the swell-ing tide, When the
2. O the soul-thrill-ing rapt-ure when I view His bless-ed face, And the
3. O the dear ones in glo - ry, how they beck-on me, to come, And our
4. Thro' the gates to the cit - y, in a robe of spot-less white He will
bright and glorious morning I shall see, I shall know my Re-deem-er when I
lus - ter of His kind-ly beam-ing eye; How my full heart will praise Him for the
part - ing at the riv - er I re - call; To the sweet vales of E-den they will
lead me where no tears will ev-er fall; In the glad song of a - ges I shall
reach the oth - er side, And His smile will be the first to wel-come me.
mer - cy, love and grace, That pre-pare for me a man-sion in the sky.
sing my wel-come home; But I long to meet my Sav - ior first of all.
min - gle with de-light; But I long to meet my Sav - ior first of all.
CHORUS.
I shall know...... Him, I shall know Him, And redeem'd by His side I shall stand,
I shall know Him

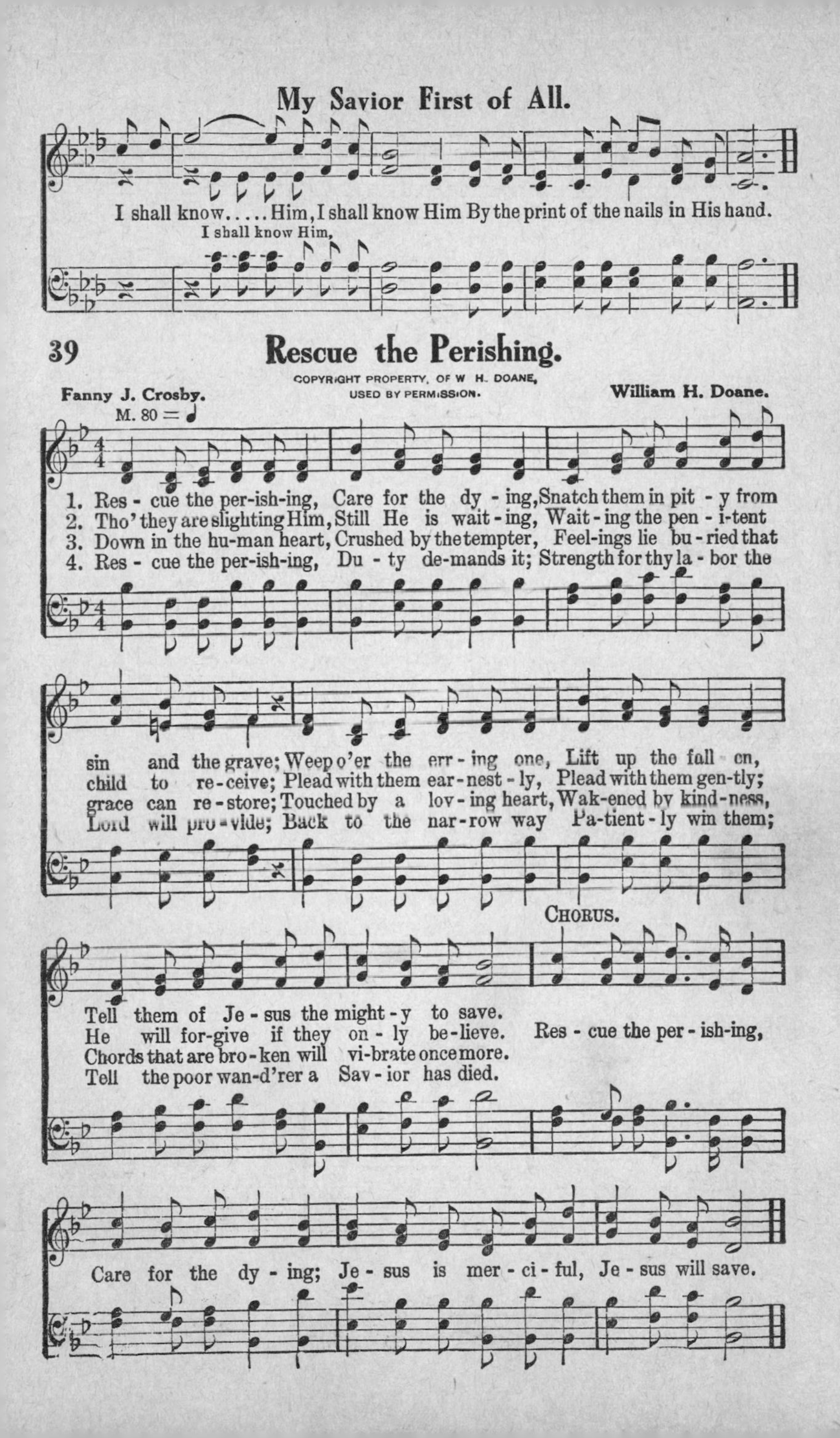
My Savior First of All.
I shall know..... Him, I shall know Him By the print of the nails in His hand.
I shall know Him,
39
Rescue the Perishing.
COPYRIGHT PROPERTY, OF W. H. DOANE,
USED BY PERMISSION.
Fanny J. Crosby.
William H. Doane.
M. 80 =
1. Res - cue the per-ish-ing, Care for the dy - ing, Snatch them in pit - y from
2. Tho' they are slighting Him, Still He is wait - ing, Wait - ing the pen - i-tent
3. Down in the hu-man heart, Crushed by the tempter, Feel-ings lie bu - ried that
4. Res - cue the per-ish-ing, Du - ty de-mands it; Strength for thy la - bor the
sin and the grave; Weep o'er the err - ing one, Lift up the fall - en,
child to re-ceive; Plead with them ear-nest - ly, Plead with them gen-tly;
grace can re-store; Touched by a lov - ing heart, Wak-ened by kind-ness,
Lord will pro - vide; Back to the nar-row way Pa-tient - ly win them;
CHORUS.
Tell them of Je - sus the might - y to save.
He will for-give if they on - ly be-lieve.
Chords that are bro-ken will vi-brate once more.
Tell the poor wan-d'rer a Sav - ior has died.
Res - cue the per - ish-ing,
Care for the dy - ing; Je - sus is mer - ci - ful, Je - sus will save.

40. Love Lifted Me.

James Rowe. Howard E. Smith.

M. 69 = ♩.
1. I was sink-ing deep in sin, Far from the peaceful shore, Ver - y deep - ly
2. All my heart to Him I give, Ev - er to Him I'll cling, In His bless-ed
3. Souls in dan-ger, look a-bove, Je - sus com-plete-ly saves; He will lift you
stained with-in, Sink - ing to rise no more; But the Mas-ter of the sea
pres - ence live, Ev - er His prais-es sing. Love so might-y and so true
by His love Out of the an - gry waves. He's the Mas-ter of the sea,
Heard my de-spair-ing cry, From the wa - ters lift-ed me, Now safe am I.
Mer - its my soul's best songs, Faith-ful, lov-ing serv-ice, too, To Him be - longs.
Bil - lows His will o - bey; He your Sav-ior wants to be—Be saved to - day.
CHORUS.
Love lift - ed me!...... Love lift - ed me!...... When noth - ing
e - ven me! e - ven me!
else could help, Love lift - ed me. Love lift - ed me.
1
2

41. Carry Your Cross With a Smile.

COPYRIGHT, 1916, BY HOMER A. RODEHEAVER.
INTERNATIONAL COPYRIGHT SECURED.
Ina Duley Ogdon.
Chas. H. Gabriel.
M. 54 = ♩.
1. Tho' your heart may be heav - y with sor - row and care, You may
2. Let the well by the way - side that flows un - to all Strength im -
3. For the work that you faith-ful - ly, will - ing - ly do, You shall
oth - ers to glad - ness be - guile, If a face like the light of the
part for each step of the mile; Let your faith the great prom - is - es
reap a re - ward af - ter - while; On - ly grace in your serv - ice can
morn - ing you wear, And car - ry your cross with a smile!
oft - en re - call, And car - ry your cross with a smile!
glo - ri - fy you, So car - ry your cross with a smile!
CHORUS.
Car - ry your cross with a smile,..... Car - ry your cross with a smile;.... You may oth - ers from
Car - ry your cross with a smile, Car - ry your cross with a smile;
sad - ness to glad - ness be - guile, If you car - ry your cross with a smile!

42. Dwelling in Beulah Land.

C. A. M.

C. Austin Miles.

M. 104 = ♩
1. Far a-way the noise of strife up-on my ear is fall-ing, Then I know the
2. Far be-low the storm of doubt up-on the world is beat-ing, Sons of men in
3. Let the storm-y breez-es blow, their cry can-not a-larm me, I am safe-ly
4. View-ing here the works of God, I sink in con-tem-pla-tion; Hear-ing now His
sins of earth be-set on ev-'ry hand; Doubt and fear and things of earth in
bat-tle long the en-e-my with-stand; Safe am I with-in the cas-tle
shel-ter'd here, pro-tect-ed by God's hand; Here the sun is al-ways shin-ing,
bless-ed voice, I see the way He plann'd; Dwell-ing in the Spir-it, here I
vain to me are call-ing, None of these shall move me from Beu-lah Land.
of God's word re-treat-ing, Noth-ing there can reach me-'tis Beu-lah Land.
Here there's naught can harm me, I am safe for-ev-er in Beu-lah Land.
learn of full sal-va-tion, Glad-ly will I tar-ry in Beu-lah Land.
CHORUS.
I'm liv-ing on the moun-tain, un-der-neath a cloud-less sky; I'm
Praise God!
drink-ing at the foun-tain that nev-er shall run dry; O yes! I'm feast-ing on the

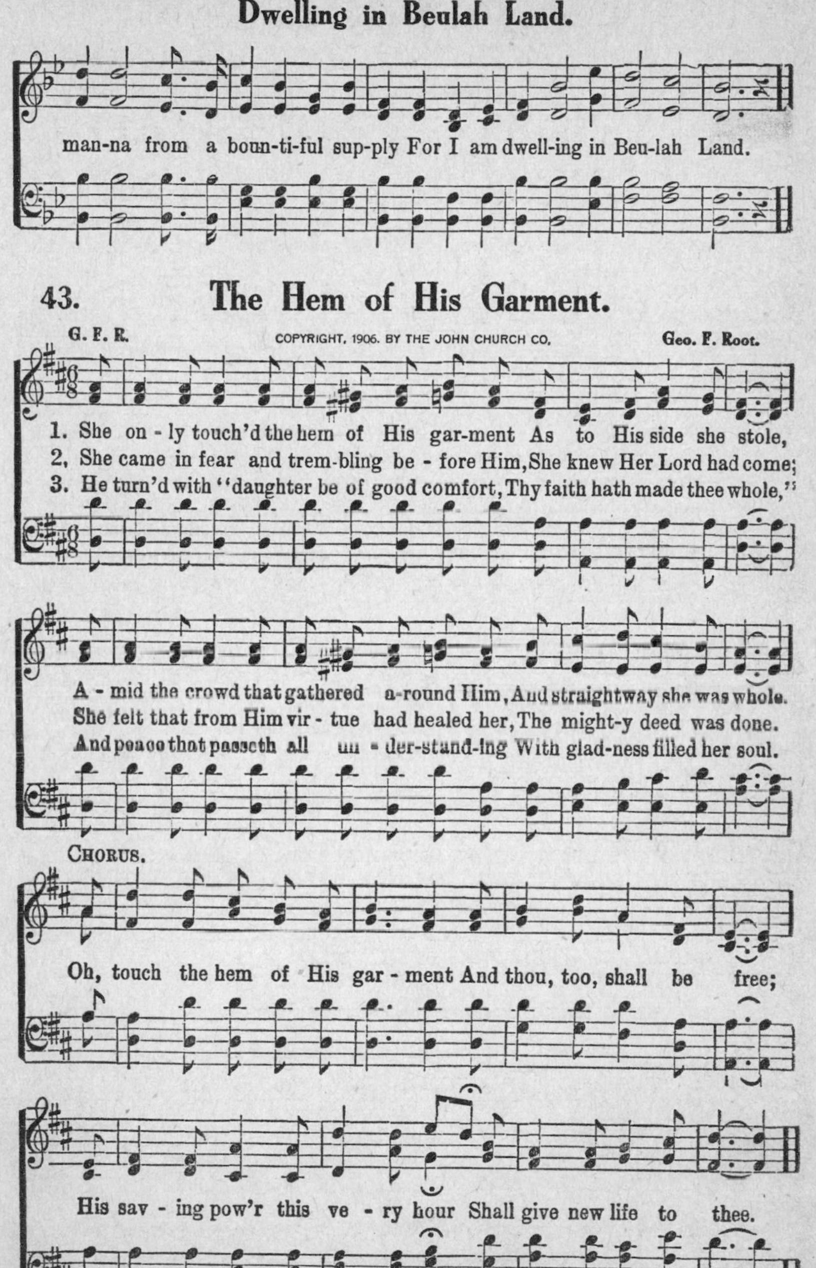
Dwelling in Beulah Land.
man-na from a boun-ti-ful sup-ply For I am dwell-ing in Beu-lah Land.
43. The Hem of His Garment.
G. F. R.
COPYRIGHT, 1906. BY THE JOHN CHURCH CO.
Geo. F. Root.
1. She on - ly touch'd the hem of His gar-ment As to His side she stole,
2, She came in fear and trem-bling be - fore Him, She knew Her Lord had come;
3. He turn'd with "daughter be of good comfort, Thy faith hath made thee whole,"
A - mid the crowd that gathered a-round Him, And straightway she was whole.
She felt that from Him vir - tue had healed her, The might-y deed was done.
And peace that passeth all un - der-stand-ing With glad-ness filled her soul.
CHORUS.
Oh, touch the hem of His gar - ment And thou, too, shall be free;
His sav - ing pow'r this ve - ry hour Shall give new life to thee.

44. The Homeland.
C. H. G.
COPYRIGHT, 1919, BY HOMER A RODEHEAVER.
INTERNATIONAL COPYRIGHT SECURED
Chas. H. Gabriel.
M. 84
1. When the beau-ties of the Homeland Burst up - on my rav-ished sight, And the
2. Gold-en streets thro-'out the cit-y, Pearl-y gates and jas - per walls, Shin-ing
3. When the sil - ver cord is loosened, When my spir - it takes its flight, And my
King in all His beau-ty I shall see,...... Then how small will seem the trials
throngs who sweetly chant their Maker's praise; Where no sickness ev - er en-ters,
soul shall from this cumb'rous clay be free,.... Just one note of heav-en's mu-sic,
Which did here my soul affright, And how radiant heav-en's splendor seems to me!
And no shad-ow ev - er falls, Naught to mar the joy of ev-er-last-ing praise.
Just one glimpse of glory bright, Will sweet recompense for all my toil-ing be.
CHORUS.
O the { Home-land o-ver yon-der, Blessed land of light and won-der, Where I
lit - tle more rough tossing, And I'll reach the river's cross-ing, And be

The Homeland.

hope to meet my Savior face to face;........ Just a
gathered in the (Omit..............................) Homeland, saved by grace.
Sav - ior, meet Him face to face;

45. What Did He Do?

Dr. J. M. Gray. W. Owen.

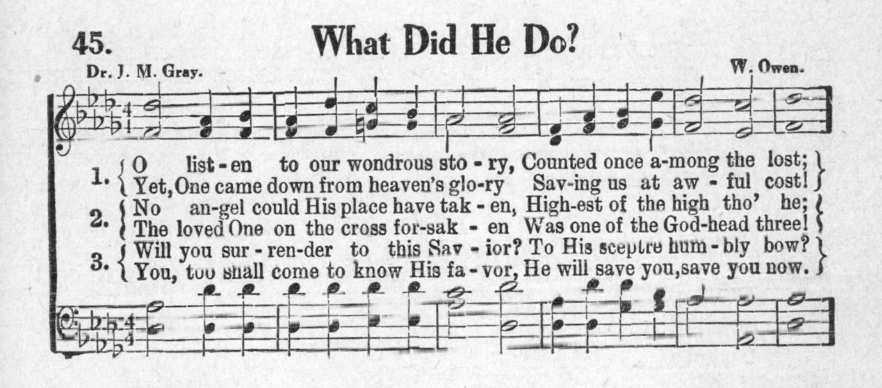
1. { O list-en to our wondrous sto-ry, Counted once a-mong the lost;
Yet, One came down from heaven's glo-ry Sav-ing us at aw-ful cost! }
2. { No an-gel could His place have tak-en, High-est of the high tho' he;
The loved One on the cross for-sak-en Was one of the God-head three! }
3. { Will you sur-ren-der to this Sav-ior? To His sceptre hum-bly bow?
You, too shall come to know His fa-vor, He will save you, save you now. }

CHORUS.

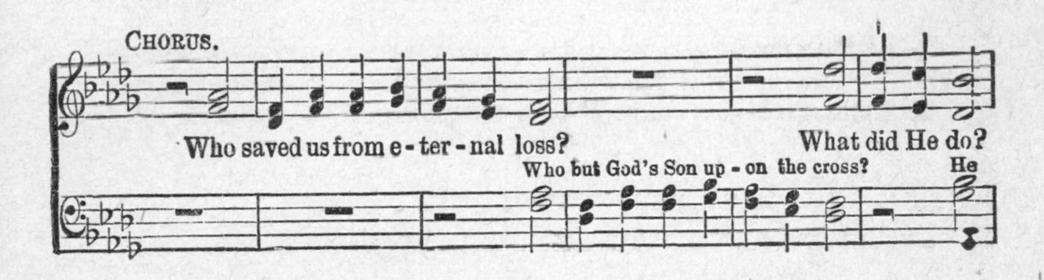
Who saved us from e-ter-nal loss? What did He do?
Who but God's Son up-on the cross? He

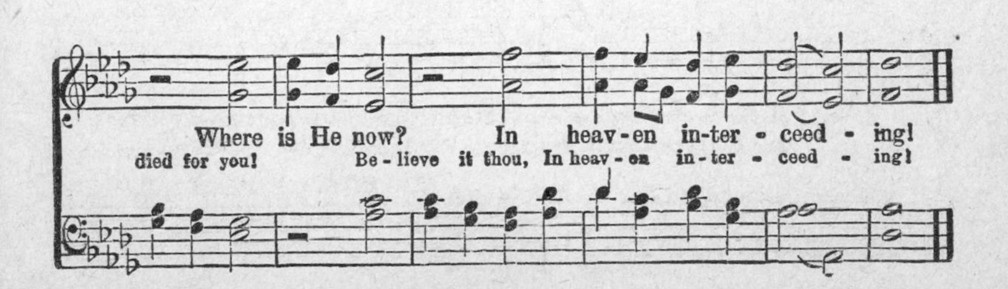
Where is He now? In heav-en in-ter-ceed-ing!
died for you! Be-lieve it thou, In heav-en in-ter-ceed-ing!

46 Brighten the Corner Where You Are.

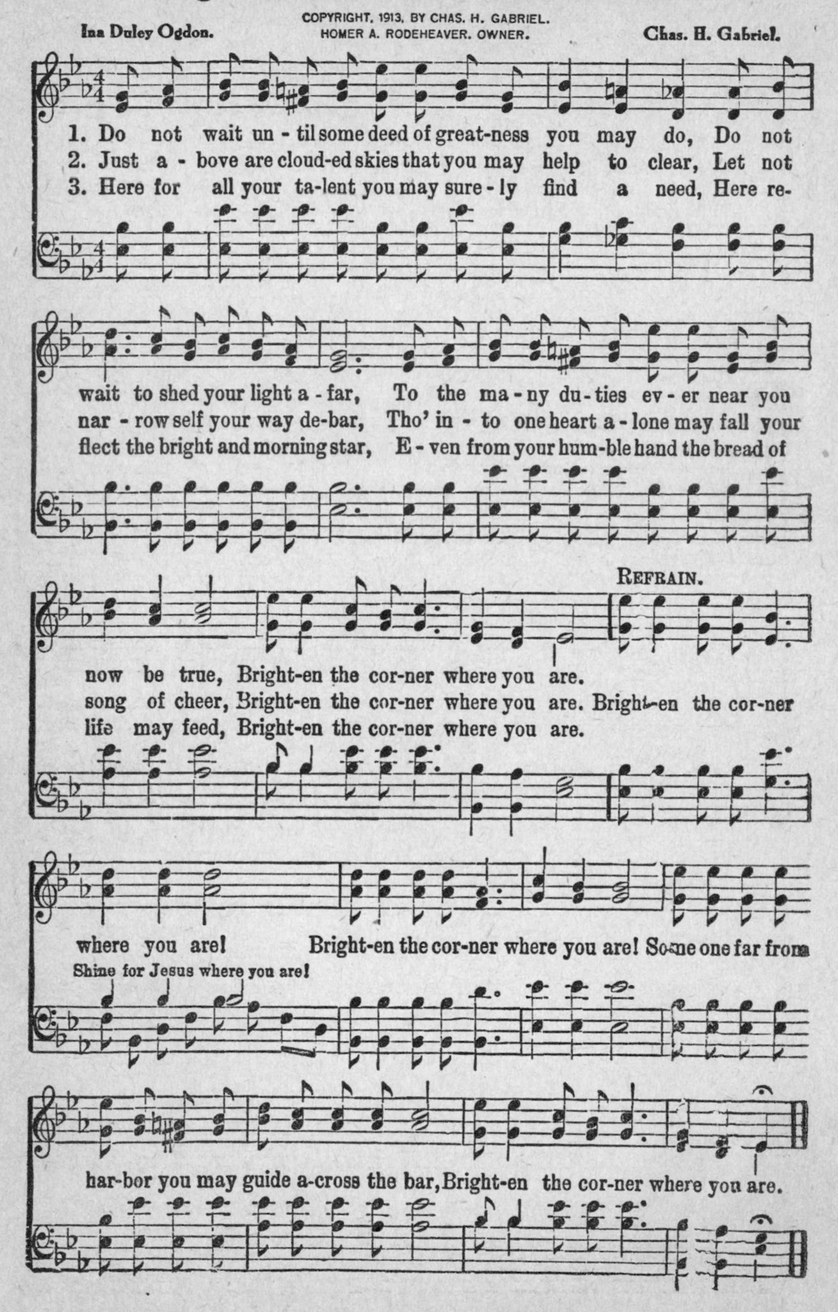
COPYRIGHT, 1913, BY CHAS. H. GABRIEL.
HOMER A. RODEHEAVER, OWNER.
Ina Duley Ogdon.
Chas. H. Gabriel.
1. Do not wait un - til some deed of great-ness you may do, Do not
2. Just a - bove are cloud-ed skies that you may help to clear, Let not
3. Here for all your ta-lent you may sure - ly find a need, Here re-
wait to shed your light a - far, To the ma - ny du - ties ev - er near you
nar - row self your way de-bar, Tho' in - to one heart a - lone may fall your
flect the bright and morning star, E - ven from your hum-ble hand the bread of
now be true, Bright-en the cor-ner where you are.
song of cheer, Bright-en the cor-ner where you are. Bright-en the cor-ner
life may feed, Bright-en the cor-ner where you are.
REFRAIN.
where you are! Bright-en the cor-ner where you are! Some one far from
Shine for Jesus where you are!
har-bor you may guide a-cross the bar, Bright-en the cor-ner where you are.

47. I Shall Be Ready.

COPYRIGHT, 1913, BY B. D. ACKLEY.
HOMER A. RODEHEAVER, OWNER
Rev. A. H. Ackley.
B. D. Ackley
M. 56 = 𝅗𝅥.
1. I shall be read - y to wel-come the Sav - ior, I may be-
2. I shall be read - y for Him I have trust - ed, Us - ing the
3. Shall His re - turn-ing to you mean a bless - ing? Or will you
4. Reign-ing with Him, He has prom-ised to make me Heir un - to
hold Him de - scend from on high, Clothed in His gar-ments of
tal - ents com - mit - ted to me; Things I once loved from my
trem - ble and fall down with fear? How will He find you, de-
God and Joint - Heir with His Son; All shall be well when He
heav - en - ly splen - dor; O what a day when the King shall draw nigh!
heart have de - part - ed, Liv - ing in Je - sus my soul is made free.
ny - ing, con - fess - ing? Seek Him, be - liev-ing, while yet He is near.
comes back to take me, Rul - er and Lord of the world He has won.
CHORUS.
I shall be read - y when Je-sus comes, When He comes, when He comes,
I shall be read-y when Je - sus comes, When Je-sus comes back for His own.

48. The Secrets of God's Grace.

COPYRIGHT, 1922, BY HOMER A. RODEHEAVER.
INTERNATIONAL COPYRIGHT SECURED.
Katherine A. Grimes.
W. C. Jordon.
M. 66 = ♩.
1. Wondrous their mys - ter - y, glo - rious their his - to - ry, Touched with the beau - ty of Je - sus' own face; Tongue can - not tell of them, tho' the heart swell with them: Such are the se - crets of God's sweet grace.
2. Sweet in their pur - i - ty, strong in their sur - e - ty, Bound by no lim - it of time or of space; Yet if in Him we hide, mat - ters not what be - tide, Ours are the se - crets of God's sweet grace.
3. Once we have known their pow'r, e'en in life's dark-est hour, Gold - en with prom - ise their glo - ry we trace; Come to Him, hide in Him, let your life bide in Him, Blest with the se - crets of God's sweet grace.
CHORUS.
Won - der-ful grace,..... oh, won - - der-ful grace;....
Won-der-ful grace, oh, wonderful grace, The secrets of God's most won-der-ful grace;
All the world o-ver may sad hearts discover The secrets of God's sweet grace.

49. King of Kings.

Psalm 136.* J. B. Herbert.

M. 96 = ♩
1. O thank the Lord, the Lord of love; O thank the God all gods a-bove;
2. Give thanks to God, for good is He, Thanks to the God of gods give ye;
3. Who tho't on us a-midst our woes, And res-cued us from all our foes;
4. O praise the Lord for He is kind, Give thanks to Him with heart and mind;
O thank the might-y King of kings, Whose arm hath done such wondrous things.
Thanks give the Lord of lords un-to, Who on-ly won-ders great can do.
Who dai-ly feeds each liv-ing thing; O thank the heav'n's Al-might-y King.
His mer-cy flows an end-less stream, To all e-ter-ni-ty the same.
CHORUS. Suggested by the "Hallelujah Chorus."
Kings of kings for ev-er and ev-er; Lord of lords, for ev-er and ev-er;
King of kings,........................ Lord of lords,..........................
King of kings for ev-er and ev-er; King of kings and Lord of lords!
King of kings,.....................

50. My Father Watches Over Me.

Rev. W. C. Martin. Chas. H. Gabriel.

1. I trust in God wher - ev-er I may be,......... Up - on the land or
2. He makes the rose an ob-ject of His care,......... He guides the ea - gle
3. I trust in God, for, in the li-on's den,......... On bat- tle-field, or
4. The val-ley may be dark, the shadows deep,...... But O, the Shep-herd
on the roll - ing sea, For, come what may, From day to day, My heav'nly
thro' the pathless air, And sure - ly He.... re-mem-bers me,—My heav'nly
in the pris-on pen, Thro' praise or blame, Thro' flood or flame, My heav'nly
guards His lonely sheep; And thro' the gloom He'll lead me home, My heav'nly
rit.
CHORUS.
Fa-ther watches o - ver me. I trust in God,—I know He cares for
me......................... On mountain bleak or on the storm-y
He cares for me, On mount-ain bleak or on the
sea;......................... Tho' bil-lows roll,........................ He keeps my
sea, the storm - y sea; tho' bil-lows roll, He

My Father Watches Over Me.

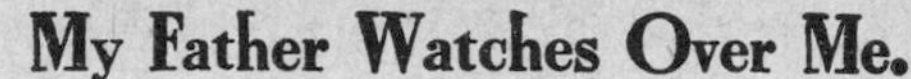

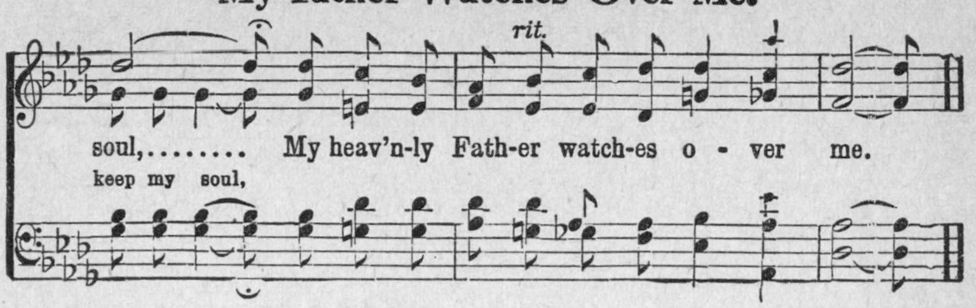
rit.
soul,........ My heav'n-ly Fath-er watch-es o - ver me.
keep my soul,

51 What a Friend.

Joseph Scriven. C. C. Converse.

M. 84 = ♩
1. What a Friend we have in Je - sus, All our sins and griefs to bear!
2. Have we tri-als and temp-ta - tions? Is there troub-le an - y-where?
3. Are we weak and heav-y - la - den, Cum-bered with a load of care?—
FINE
What a priv - i - lege to car - ry Ev - 'ry-thing to God in prayer!
D.S.-All be-cause we do not car - ry Ev - 'ry-thing to God in prayer.
We should nev - er be dis - cour - aged, Take it to the Lord in prayer.
D.S.-Je - sus knows our ev - 'ry weak - ness, Take it to the Lord in prayer.
Pre - cious Sav-ior, still our ref - uge,—Take it to the Lord in prayer.
D.S.-In His arms He'll take and shield thee, Thou wilt find a sol - ace there.
D.S.
O what peace we oft - en for - feit, O what need-less pain we bear,
Can we find a friend so faith - ful Who will all our sor-rows share?
Do thy friends de-spise, for-sake thee? Take it to the Lord in prayer;

52.

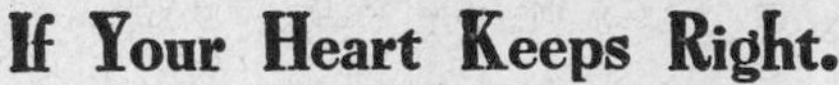
If Your Heart Keeps Right.

Lizzie DeArmond. B. D. Ackley.

M. 96 = ♩
1. If the dark shad-ows gath-er As you go a-long, Do not grieve for their
2. Is your life just a tan-gle, Full of toil and care? Smile a bit as you
3. There are blossoms of gladness 'Neath the winter's snow; From the gloom and the
com-ing, Sing a cheer-y song! There is joy for the tak-ing; It will
jour-ney, Oth-ers' bur-dens share; You'll for-get all your troubles, Mak-ing
dark-ness Comes the morning's glow; Nev-er give up the bat-tle, You will
soon be light,—Ev-'ry cloud wears a rain-bow, If your heart keeps right.
their lives bright; Skies will grow blue and sun-ny, If your heart keeps right.
win the fight, Gain the rest of the Vic-tor, If your heart keeps right.
CHORUS.
If your heart keeps right, If your heart keeps right, There's a song of
glad-ness in the dark-est night; If your heart keeps right, If your

If Your Heart Keeps Right.
heart keeps right, Ev-'ry cloud will wear a rain-bow, If your heart keeps right.
53.
Open the Gates of Prayer.
COPYRIGHT, 1917, BY HOMER A. RODEHEAVER.
INTERNATIONAL COPYRIGHT SECURED.
Fanny J. Crosby.
Chas. H. Gabriel.
M. 56 =
1. Je-sus, my Lord, Thy voice I hear Bidding me now by faith draw near,
2. Je-sus, my trust, this heart is Thine, Kept by the pow'r of grace di - vine;
3. Je-sus, my life, O guide my way On-ward from earth to end - less day.
Near to the fount so pure with-in, Cleans-ing my soul from ev - 'ry sin.
Help me to rise my cares a-bove, Filled with Thy deep, un - bound - ed love.
Soon may I reach the heav'n-ly shore, There to a - bide for - ev - er-more.
CHORUS.
Je-sus, my Lord, I come to Thee; O-pen the gate of prayer for me!
I come to Thee, I come to Thee, O-pen the gate of prayer for me.

54. There is Glory in My Soul!

Grace Weiser Davis.
COPYRIGHT, 1922, BY CHAS. H. GABRIEL. RENEWAL.
HOMER A. RODEHEAVER, OWNER.
Chas. H. Gabriel.
M. 108 = ♩
1. Since I lost my sins and I found my Sav - ior, There is glo - ry
2. Since He cleansed my heart, gave me sight for blind-ness, There is glo - ry
3. Since with God I've walked, hav-ing sweet com-mun - ion, There is glo - ry
4. Since I en-tered Canaan on my way to heav - en, There is glo - ry
in my soul! Since by faith I sought and ob-tained God's fa - vor, There is
in my soul! Since He touched and healed me in lov - ing kind-ness, There is
in my soul! Bright-er grows each day in this heav'n-ly un - ion, There is
in my soul! Since the day my life to the Lord was giv - en, There is
glo-ry in my soul!
CHORUS.
There is glo - ry, glo-ry, there is glo - ry in my soul!
Ev-'ry day brighter grows, And I con-quer all my foes; There is glo - ry,
glo-ry, there is glo - ry in my soul! There is glo - ry in my soul!
glo-ry in my soul!

55. There is Power in the Blood.

L. E. J. — COPYRIGHT, 1899, BY H. L. GILMOUR, WENONAH, N. J. — L. E. Jones.

M. 100 = ♩

1. Would you be free from your bur-den of sin? There's pow'r in the blood, pow'r in the blood; Would you o'er e-vil a vic-to-ry win? There's won-der-ful pow'r in the blood.
2. Would you be free from your passion and pride? There's pow'r in the blood, pow'r in the blood; Come for a cleans-ing to Cal-va-ry's tide,
3. Would you be whit-er, much whit-er than snow? There's pow'r in the blood, pow'r in the blood; Sin-stains are lost in its life-giv-ing flow,
4. Would you do serv-ice for Je-sus your King? There's pow'r in the blood, pow'r in the blood; Would you live dai-ly, His prais-es to sing?

CHORUS.

There is pow'r, pow'r, (There is pow'r,) Wonder-working pow'r in the blood (in the blood) of the Lamb; (of the Lamb;) There is pow'r, pow'r, (There is pow'r,) Wonder-working pow'r In the pre-cious blood of the Lamb.

A New Name in Glory.

C. A. M. C. Austin Miles.

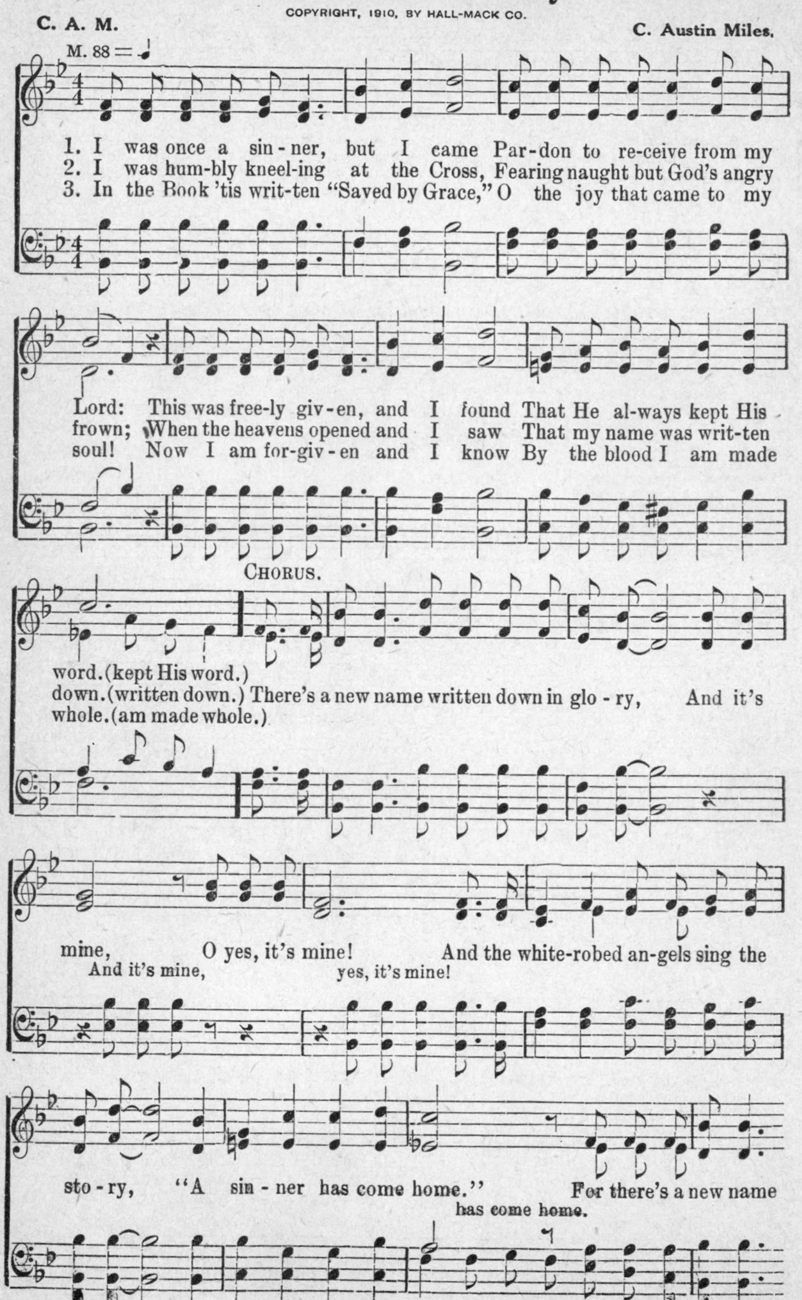
M. 88 = ♩
1. I was once a sin - ner, but I came Par-don to re-ceive from my
2. I was hum-bly kneel-ing at the Cross, Fearing naught but God's angry
3. In the Book 'tis writ-ten "Saved by Grace," O the joy that came to my
Lord: This was free-ly giv - en, and I found That He al-ways kept His
frown; When the heavens opened and I saw That my name was writ-ten
soul! Now I am for-giv - en and I know By the blood I am made
CHORUS.
word. (kept His word.)
down. (written down.) There's a new name written down in glo - ry, And it's
whole. (am made whole.)
mine, O yes, it's mine! And the white-robed an-gels sing the
And it's mine, yes, it's mine!
sto - ry, "A sin - ner has come home." For there's a new name
has come home.

A New Name in Glory.
writ-ten down in glo - ry, And it's mine, O yes, it's mine!
And it's mine, yes, it's mine!
With my sins for-giv-en I am bound for heav-en, Nev - er-more to roam.
57 Near the Cross.
Fanny J. Crosby.
USED BY PERMISSION.
W. H. Doane.
M. 50
1. Je - sus, keep me near the Cross! There a pre - cious foun - tain,
2. Near the Cross, a trem-bling soul, Love and mer - cy found me;
3. Near the Cross! O Lamb of God, Bring its scenes be - fore me;
4. Near the Cross I'll watch and pray, Hop - ing, trust - ing ev - er,
FINE.
Free to all— a heal - ing stream, Flows from Cal-v'ry's moun - tain.
There the Bright and Morn - ing Star Sheds its beams a - round me.
Help me walk from day to day, With its shad - ows o'er me.
Till I reach the gold - en strand, Just be - yond the riv - er.
D.S.—Till my rap - tured soul shall find Rest be - yond the riv - er.
CHORUS.
D.S.
In the cross, in the cross, Be my glo - ry ev - er,

58. I Know Whom I Have Believed.

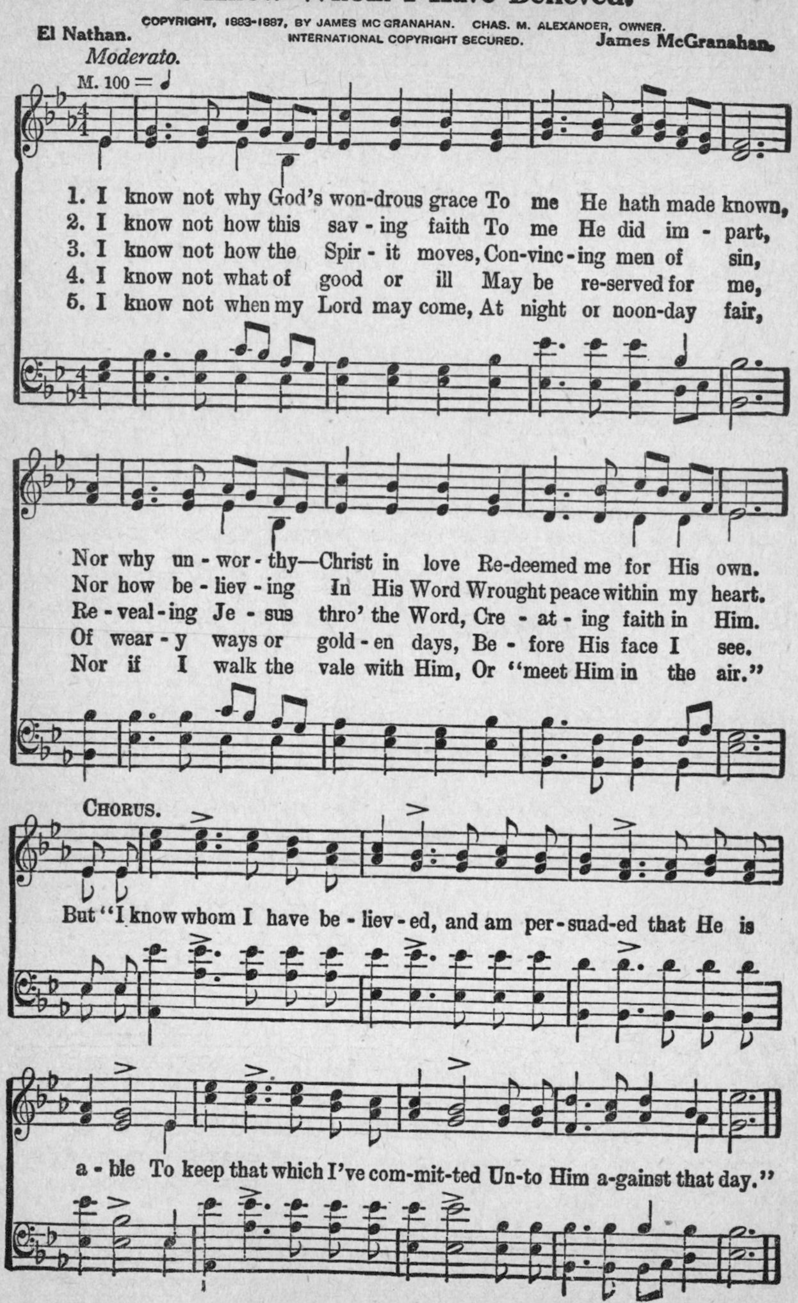
COPYRIGHT, 1883-1887, BY JAMES MC GRANAHAN. CHAS. M. ALEXANDER, OWNER.
INTERNATIONAL COPYRIGHT SECURED.
El Nathan.
James McGranahan.
Moderato.
M. 100 = ♩
1. I know not why God's won-drous grace To me He hath made known,
2. I know not how this sav - ing faith To me He did im - part,
3. I know not how the Spir - it moves, Con-vinc - ing men of sin,
4. I know not what of good or ill May be re-served for me,
5. I know not when my Lord may come, At night or noon-day fair,
Nor why un - wor - thy—Christ in love Re-deemed me for His own.
Nor how be - liev - ing In His Word Wrought peace within my heart.
Re - veal - ing Je - sus thro' the Word, Cre - at - ing faith in Him.
Of wear - y ways or gold - en days, Be - fore His face I see.
Nor if I walk the vale with Him, Or "meet Him in the air."
CHORUS.
But "I know whom I have be - liev - ed, and am per - suad-ed that He is
a - ble To keep that which I've com-mit-ted Un-to Him a-gainst that day."

59.

Somebody Cares.

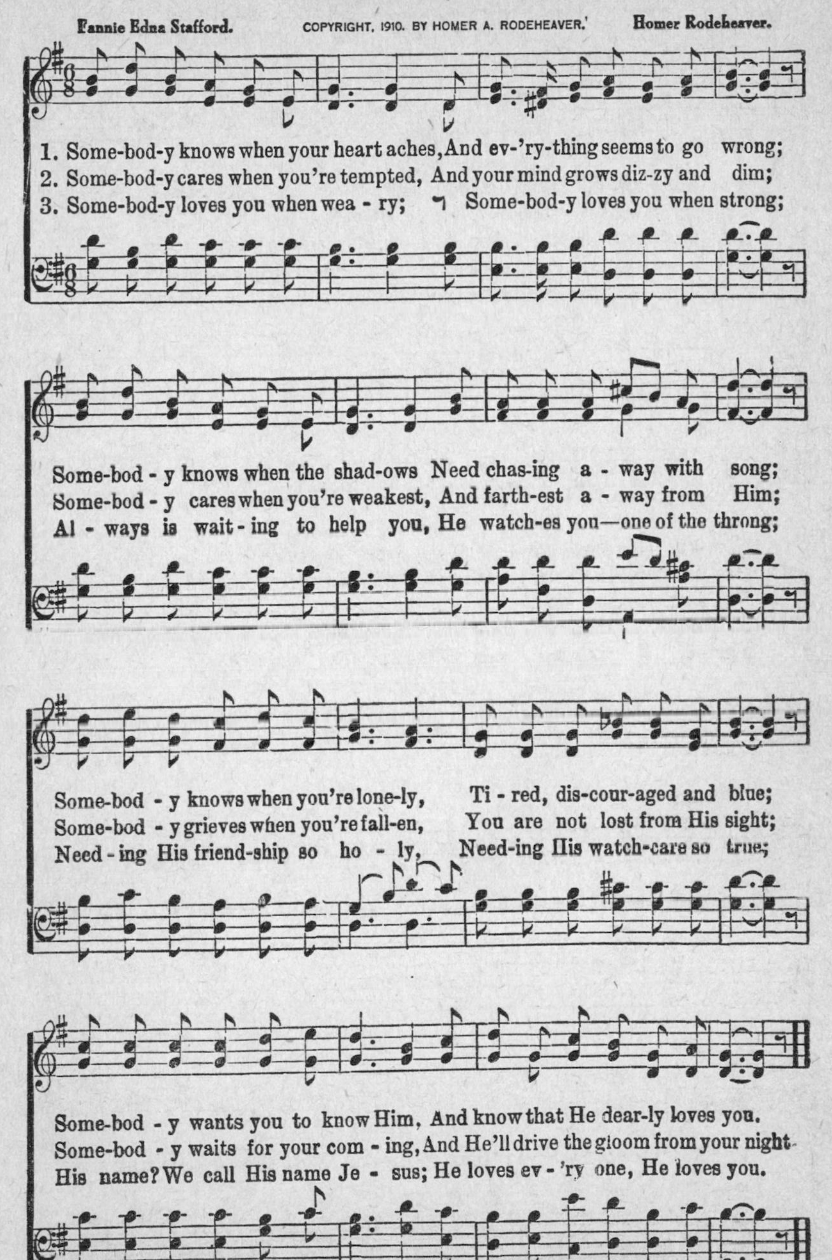
Fannie Edna Stafford.
COPYRIGHT, 1910, BY HOMER A. RODEHEAVER.
Homer Rodeheaver.
1. Some-bod-y knows when your heart aches, And ev-'ry-thing seems to go wrong;
2. Some-bod-y cares when you're tempted, And your mind grows diz-zy and dim;
3. Some-bod-y loves you when wea - ry; Some-bod-y loves you when strong;
Some-bod - y knows when the shad-ows Need chas-ing a - way with song;
Some-bod - y cares when you're weakest, And farth-est a - way from Him;
Al - ways is wait - ing to help you, He watch-es you—one of the throng;
Some-bod - y knows when you're lone-ly, Ti - red, dis-cour-aged and blue;
Some-bod - y grieves when you're fall-en, You are not lost from His sight;
Need - ing His friend-ship so ho - ly, Need-ing His watch-care so true;
Some-bod - y wants you to know Him, And know that He dear-ly loves you.
Some-bod - y waits for your com - ing, And He'll drive the gloom from your night.
His name? We call His name Je - sus; He loves ev - 'ry one, He loves you.

60 Jesus, Lover of My Soul.

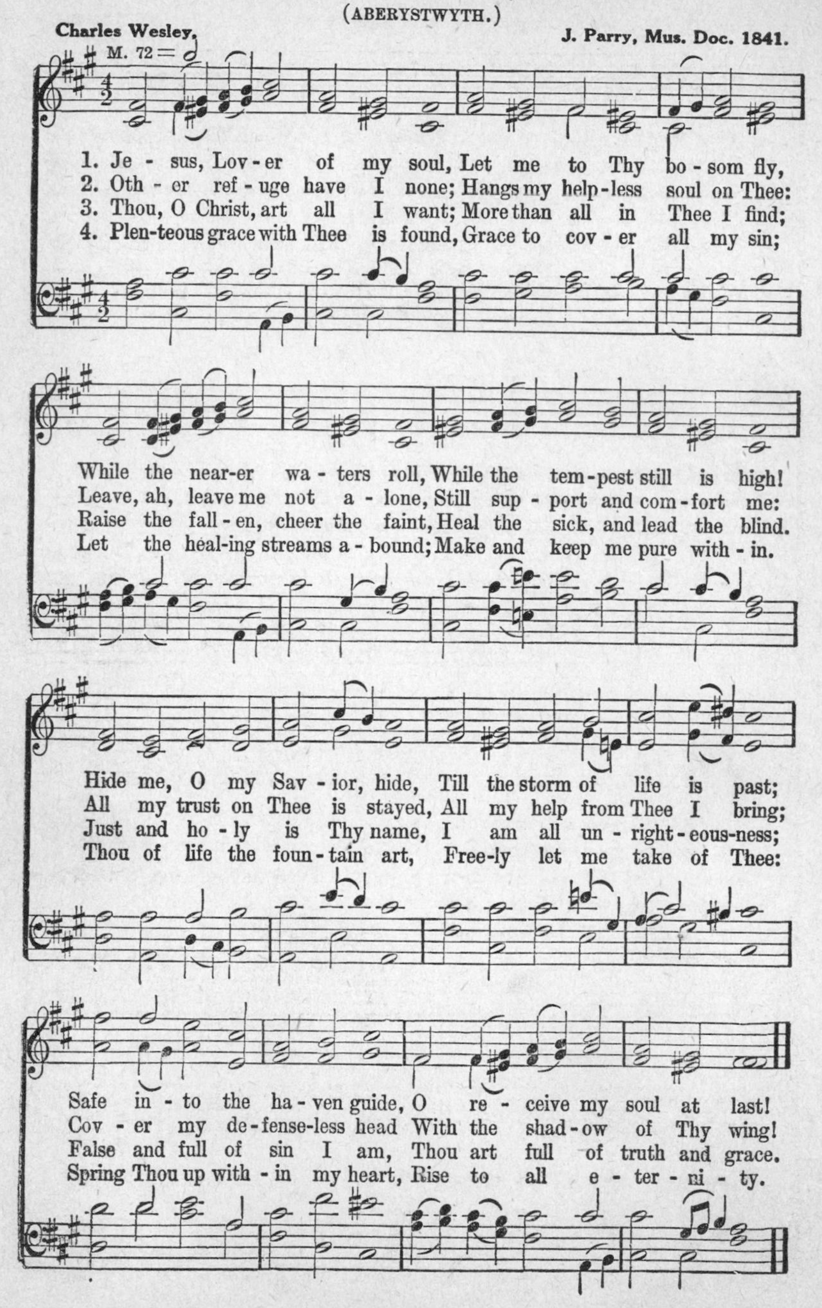
(ABERYSTWYTH.)
Charles Wesley.
J. Parry, Mus. Doc. 1841.
M. 72 =
1. Je - sus, Lov - er of my soul, Let me to Thy bo - som fly,
2. Oth - er ref - uge have I none; Hangs my help - less soul on Thee:
3. Thou, O Christ, art all I want; More than all in Thee I find;
4. Plen-teous grace with Thee is found, Grace to cov - er all my sin;
While the near-er wa - ters roll, While the tem-pest still is high!
Leave, ah, leave me not a - lone, Still sup - port and com - fort me:
Raise the fall - en, cheer the faint, Heal the sick, and lead the blind.
Let the heal-ing streams a - bound; Make and keep me pure with - in.
Hide me, O my Sav - ior, hide, Till the storm of life is past;
All my trust on Thee is stayed, All my help from Thee I bring;
Just and ho - ly is Thy name, I am all un - right - eous-ness;
Thou of life the foun - tain art, Free-ly let me take of Thee:
Safe in - to the ha - ven guide, O re - ceive my soul at last!
Cov - er my de-fense-less head With the shad - ow of Thy wing!
False and full of sin I am, Thou art full of truth and grace.
Spring Thou up with - in my heart, Rise to all e - ter - ni - ty.

61. Trust and Obey.

J. H. Sammis.
Copyright, 1887, by D. B. Towner.
D. B. Towner.
1. When we walk with the Lord In the light of His Word, What a glo-ry He
2. Not a shad-ow can rise, Not a cloud in the skies, But His smile quickly
3. Not a bur-den we bear, Not a sor-row we share, But our toil He doth
4. But we nev-er can prove The de-lights of His love Un-til all on the
5. Then in fel-low-ship sweet We will sit at His feet, Or we'll walk by His
sheds on our way! While we do His good will He a-bides with us still,
drives it a-way; Not a doubt nor a fear, Not a sigh nor a tear
rich-ly re-pay; Not a grief nor a loss, Not a frown nor a cross
al-tar we lay; For the fa-vor He shows And the joy He be-stows
side in the way; What He says we will do, Where He sends we will go,—
Chorus.
And with all who will trust and o-bey.
Can a-bide while we trust and o-bey.
But is blest if we trust and o-bey.
Are for those who will trust and o-bey.
Nev-er fear, on-ly trust and o-bey.
Trust and o-bey, for there's
no oth-er way To be hap-py in Je-sus but to trust and o-bey!

62. Drifting.

E. E. Hewitt.
COPYRIGHT, 1917, BY HOMER A. RODEHEAVER
INTERNATIONAL COPYRIGHT SECURED.
B. D. Ackley.
DUET.
M. 112 = ♩
1. Drift - ing care-less - ly with the tide, Drift - ing o - ver the wa-ters wide,
2. Drift - ing al-most up - on the bar, Los - ing sight of the Bea-con Star;
3. Drift - ing on, with no shore in view, Think not skies will be al-ways blue;
4. Drift no lon-ger! let Je - sus save, Let Him guide you a-cross the wave,
With no Cap-tain your course to guide, Drift - ing o - ver life's sea.....
From the ha-ven of joy a - far, Drift - ing o - ver life's sea.....
Storm and ship-wreck will come to you, Drift - ing o - ver life's sea.....
Lest you sink in a sin - ner's grave, Drift - ing o - ver life's sea.....
CHORUS
Drift-ing, drift-ing, no port in sight! Drift-ing far from the gos-pel light;
Lest you go down in the storm - y night; Drift-ing o - ver life's sea.

63. A Rainbow On the Cloud.
COPYRIGHT, 1914, BY CHAS. H. GABRIEL.
HOMER A. RODEHEAVER, OWNER.
E. E. Hewitt.
Chas. H. Gabriel.
M. 96 = 𝅗𝅥
1. Be not wea-ry or cast down When the heavens seem to frown, There's a
2. He whose word re-buked the storm, Now is a - ble to per-form Ev - 'ry
3. There's a rain-bow on the cloud! Tho' your soul is sorrow-bowed, Lift your
rain-bow on the cloud for you! 'Tis an arch of promise bright, Earnest, of un-fad-ing
word He whispers to your heart; Wholly lean up-on Him then, For the sun will shine a-
voice to praise the Lord to - day; There's a rainbow 'round the throne; In its glo-ry we will
light, Pour-ing from a sky of ra-diant blue.
gain, And the shadows ev-er-more de - part.
own That He led us in His per-fect way.
CHORUS.
There's a rainbow on the cloud for
on the
you, There's a prom-ise that is sure and true; Yes, the storm will pass a-
cloud for you, that is sure and true;
way; There will dawn a bright-er day–There's a rainbow on the cloud for you.

64.
Let the Joy Overflow.
COPYRIGHT, 1917, BY HOMER A. RODEHEAVER
INTERNATIONAL COPYRIGHT SECURED.
E. E. Hewitt.
Dr. S. B. Jackson.
M. 132 = ♩
1. There's a clear foun-tain flowing From the bright throne above, And its waters are glow-ing With the sun-shine of love; Take the blest con - so-la-tion, Which the Lord will be-stow, Take the cup of sal - va-tion—Let the joy o - ver-flow.
2. Man - y hearts need the sto-ry—Are a-thirst for His grace; Go to them with His glo - ry Shin-ing out from your face; Tell of Je - sus your Sav-ior! If His mer-cies you know, Show the light of His fa - vor—Let the joy o - ver-flow.
3. Be our lives free - ly yield - ed To the Savior's command; By His care ev - er shield-ed And up-held by His hand; In the path-ways of sadness, Sweetest lil - ies may grow; Let us sow seeds of glad-ness—Let the joy o - ver-flow.
CHORUS.
O the joy! . . . . . . With this wondrous sal-va-tion Be our hearts all a - glow;
O the joy!
O the joy! . . . . Let the blessing run o - ver, And joy o - ver-flow.
O the joy!

65. We're Marching to Zion.

COPYRIGHT PROPERTY OF MARY RUNYON LOWRY.

Rev. I. Watts. Rev. Robert Lowry.

1. Come, we that love the Lord, And let our joys be known, Join in a song with sweet accord, Join in a song with sweet accord, And thus surround the throne, And thus surround the throne.
2. Let those re - fuse to sing Who nev-er knew our God; But children of the heav'n-ly King, But chil-dren of the heav'nly King, May speak their joys abroad, May speak their joys abroad.
3. The hill of Zi - on yields A thou-sand sacred sweets, Before we reach the heav'n-ly fields, Before we reach the heav'nly fields, Or walk the gold-en streets, Or walk the gold-en streets.
4. Then let our songs a-bound, And ev-'ry tear be dry; We're marching thro' Im-manuel's ground, We're marching thro' Immanuel's ground, To fair - er worlds on high, To fair - er worlds on high.
And thus surround the throne, And thus sur - round the throne.
CHORUS.
We're marching to Zi-on, Beau - ti-ful, beau-ti-ful Zi-on; We're marching upward to Zi - on, The beau-ti - ful cit - y of God.
We're marching on to Zi - on,
Zi-on, Zi-on,

66. 

One Day.

Dr. J. Wilbur Chapman. Chas. H. Marsh.

1. One day when heav - en was fill'd with His prais-es, One day when sin
2. One day they led Him up Cal - va - ry's mountain, One day they nailed
3. One day they left Him a - lone in the gar - den, One day He rest-
4. One day when full - ness of time was fast dawn-ing, One day the stone
5. One day He's com - ing! for Him I am long - ing; One day the skies
was as black as could be, Je - sus came forth to be
Him for me on the tree; Won - der - ful Coun - sel - lor
ed from suf - fer - ing free, An - gels came down then to
moved a - way from the door; Then He a - rose, o - ver
with His glo - ry will shine; Won - der - ful day, my be-
born of a vir - gin, Lived, loved and labored—my Teach-er is He.
they had ac-claim'd Him, Now He is Je - sus—my Je - sus is He.
keep sa - cred vig - il, Weight-ed with sins, my Re-deem - er is He.
death He had conquered, Now He's as-cend-ed, my Lord ev - er - more.
lov - ed ones bring-ing; Hope of the hope-less, this Je - sus is mine.
CHORUS.
Liv - ing He loved me, dy - ing He saved me, Bur-ied He car - ried my
sins far a - way; Ris - ing He jus - ti - fied, free - ly for-

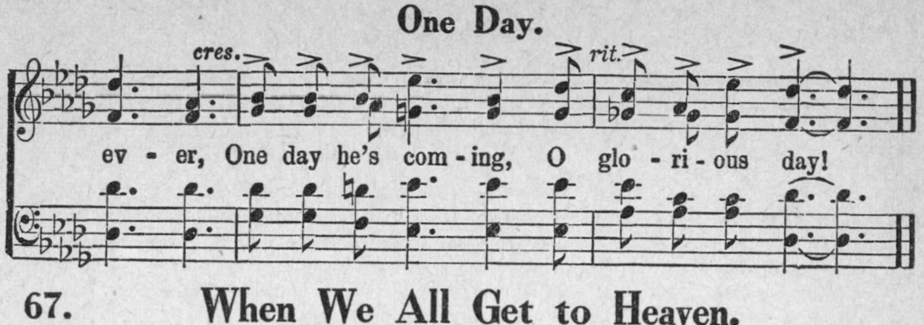
One Day.
cres.
rit.
ev - er, One day he's com - ing, O glo - ri - ous day!

67. When We All Get to Heaven.

E. E. Hewitt. Mrs. J. G. Wilson.

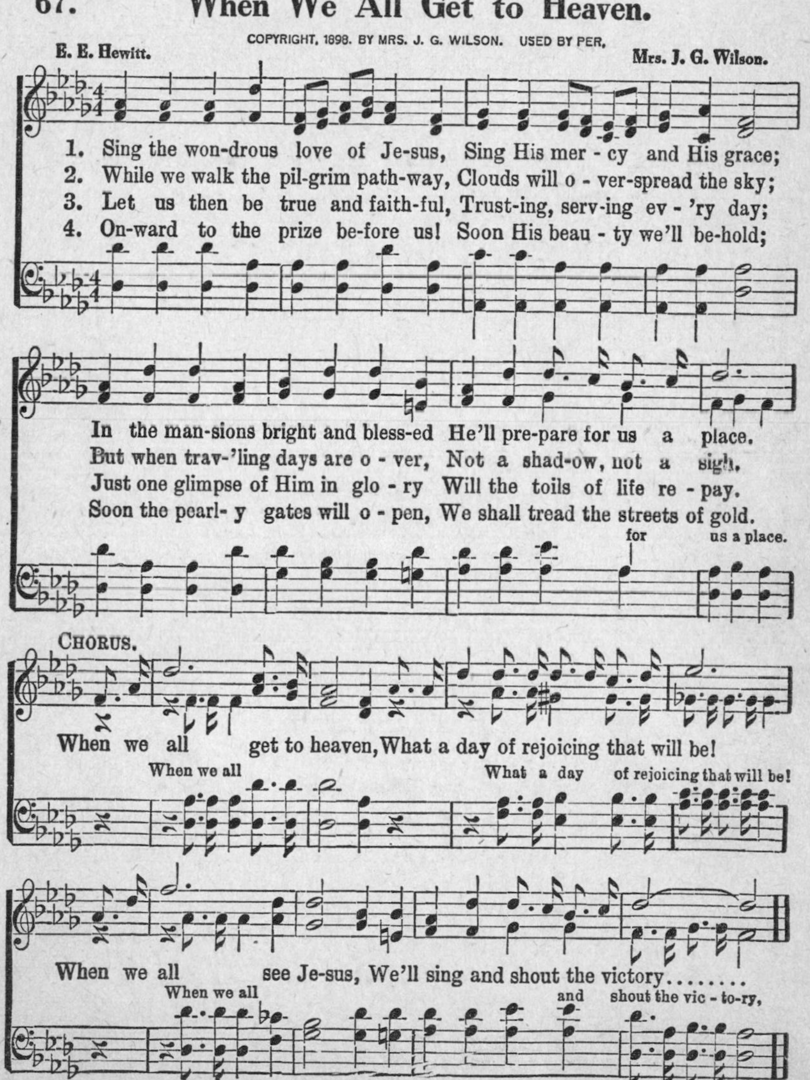
1. Sing the won-drous love of Je-sus, Sing His mer - cy and His grace;
2. While we walk the pil-grim path-way, Clouds will o - ver-spread the sky;
3. Let us then be true and faith-ful, Trust-ing, serv-ing ev - 'ry day;
4. On-ward to the prize be-fore us! Soon His beau - ty we'll be-hold;
In the man-sions bright and bless-ed He'll pre-pare for us a place.
But when trav-'ling days are o - ver, Not a shad-ow, not a sigh.
Just one glimpse of Him in glo - ry Will the toils of life re - pay.
Soon the pearl- y gates will o - pen, We shall tread the streets of gold.
for us a place.
CHORUS.
When we all get to heaven, What a day of rejoicing that will be!
When we all
What a day of rejoicing that will be!
When we all see Je-sus, We'll sing and shout the victory........
When we all
and shout the vic - to-ry,

68. Wonderful Power.

COPYRIGHT, 1917, BY HOMER A. RODEHEAVER
INTERNATIONAL COPYRIGHT SECURED.
E. E. Hewitt.
Chas. H. Gabriel.
M 56 = ♩.
1. Won-der-ful pow'r of my won-der-ful King! Mer-cy un-bound-ed, I
2. Won-der-ful pow'r of the pray'r-hear-ing Lord; Tri-als a claim on His
3. Won-der-ful pow'r that will guide me a-right, Lead me from the shadows to
4. A-ble and will-ing, O Sav-ior art Thou! A-ble and will-ing to
grate-ful-ly sing; From all the bil-lows that round me may roll,
grace will af-ford; On my dear Sav-ior I cast ev-'ry care,
mar-vel-ous light; In fierce temp-ta-tions, my ref-uge and stay,
save me just now; When earth-ly path-ways no lon-ger I roam,
Chours.
A-ble and will-ing to res-cue my soul.
A-ble and will-ing to an-swer my prayer. Won-der-ful pow'r,
A-ble and will-ing to keep me each day.
A-ble and will-ing to wel-come me home.
won-der-ful pow'r! Sav-ing me, keep-ing me, life's ev-'ry hour; Glad-ly I
sing, trust-ful-ly sing, Won-der-ful pow'r of my won-der-ful King.

69. Mother's Prayers Have Followed Me.

COPYRIGHT, 1912, BY B. D. ACKLEY.
HOMER A. RODEHEAVER, OWNER
Lizzie DeArmond.
B. D. Ackley.
M. 60 =
1. I grieved my Lord from day to day, I scorned His love so full and
2. O'er des-ert wild, o'er moun-tain high, A wan-der - er I chose to
3. He turned my dark - ness in - to light, This bless-ed Christ of Cal - va-
free, And tho' I wan - dered far a - way, My moth-er's
be; A wretch - ed soul, con-demned to die, Still moth-er's
ry! I'll praise His name both day and night, That moth-er's
CHORUS.
pray'rs have fol-lowed me. I'm com - ing home, I'm com ing
home, To live my wast - ed life a - new, For moth-er's
pray'rs have fol-lowed me, Have fol-lowed me the whole world through.

70. Saved!

H. E. B.
COPYRIGHT, 1913, BY HOMER A. RODEHEAVER.
Rev. H. E. Bright.
1. Je - sus my Sav - ior came to save me When I was wan-d'ring
2. Je - sus my Sav - ior came to cleanse me, Car - nal in heart and
3. Je - sus my Sav - ior came to guide me, O - ver the mount-ains;
4. Je - sus my Sav - ior soon will call me Home to my man - sion,
out in the night; Rich - es of glo - ry free - ly gave me,
fightings with - in; Now I en - joy His pre-cious ful - ness
down thro' the vale; Still He is with me, strong to keep me;
shin - ing a - bove; There shall I see Him in His glo - ry,
Flood-ed my soul with His won-drous light.
Pow - er and vic - t'ry o'er in - bred sin.
Fol - low-ing Him I shall nev - er fail.
Praise and a - dore Him in songs of love.
CHORUS.
I'm saved! saved!
this is my sto - ry:—Je-sus my Sav-ior cleanses and keeps me! I'm
saved! saved! filled with His glo-ry! Glo-ry to Je-sus, His grace is free.

71. My Savior's Love.

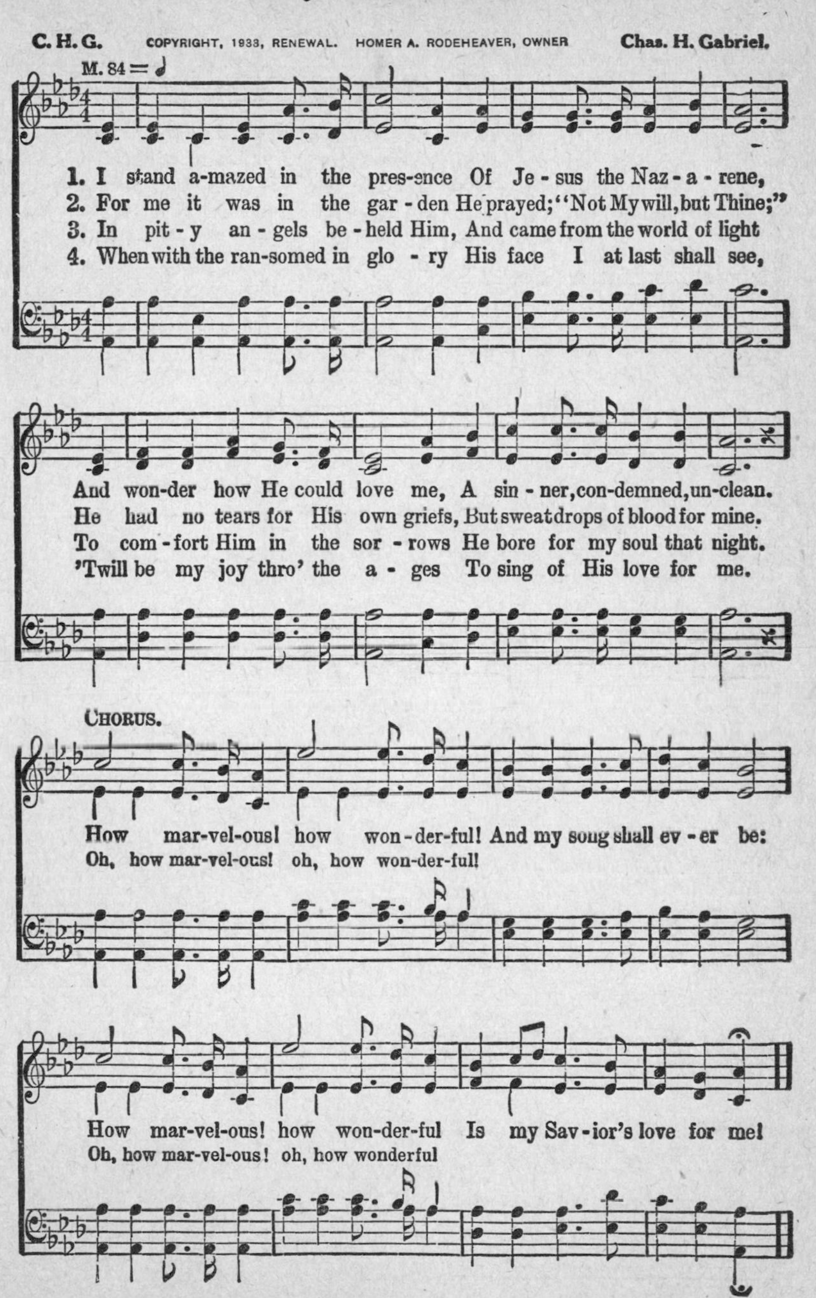
C. H. G.
COPYRIGHT, 1933, RENEWAL. HOMER A. RODEHEAVER, OWNER
Chas. H. Gabriel.
M. 84 = ♩
1. I stand a-mazed in the pres-ence Of Je-sus the Naz-a-rene,
2. For me it was in the gar-den He prayed; "Not My will, but Thine;"
3. In pit-y an-gels be-held Him, And came from the world of light
4. When with the ran-somed in glo-ry His face I at last shall see,
And won-der how He could love me, A sin-ner, con-demned, un-clean.
He had no tears for His own griefs, But sweat drops of blood for mine.
To com-fort Him in the sor-rows He bore for my soul that night.
'Twill be my joy thro' the a-ges To sing of His love for me.
CHORUS.
How mar-vel-ous! how won-der-ful! And my song shall ev-er be:
Oh, how mar-vel-ous! oh, how won-der-ful!
How mar-vel-ous! how won-der-ful Is my Sav-ior's love for me!
Oh, how mar-vel-ous! oh, how wonderful

I Am Praying for You.

S. O'Maley Gluff.
Ira D. Sankey.
M. 100 = ♩
1. I have a Sav-ior, He's plead-ing in glo - ry, A dear, lov-ing Sav-
2. I have a Fa - ther; to me He has giv - en A hope for e - ter-
3. I have a robe; 'tis re - splen-dent in white-ness, A - wait - ing in glo-
4. When Je-sus has found you, tell oth-ers the sto - ry, That my lov-ing Sav-
ior, tho' earth-friends be few; And now He is watch-ing in ten - der-ness
ni - ty, bless - ed and true; And soon will He call me to meet Him in
ry my won - der-ing view: Oh, when I re - ceive it all shin - ing in
ior is your Sav-ior, too; Then pray that your Sav - ior will bring them to
o'er me, And, oh, that my Sav-ior were your Sav-ior, too.
heav - en, But, oh, that He'd let me bring you with me, too!
bright-ness, Dear friend, could I see you re - ceiv - ing one, too!
glo - ry, And pray'r will be answered—'twas answered for you!
f CHORUS.
For you I am pray-ing, For you I am pray-ing, For you I am praying, I'm pray-ing for you.
p
f
pp rall.

The Promised Land.

Samuel Stennett. Arr. from Dunham.

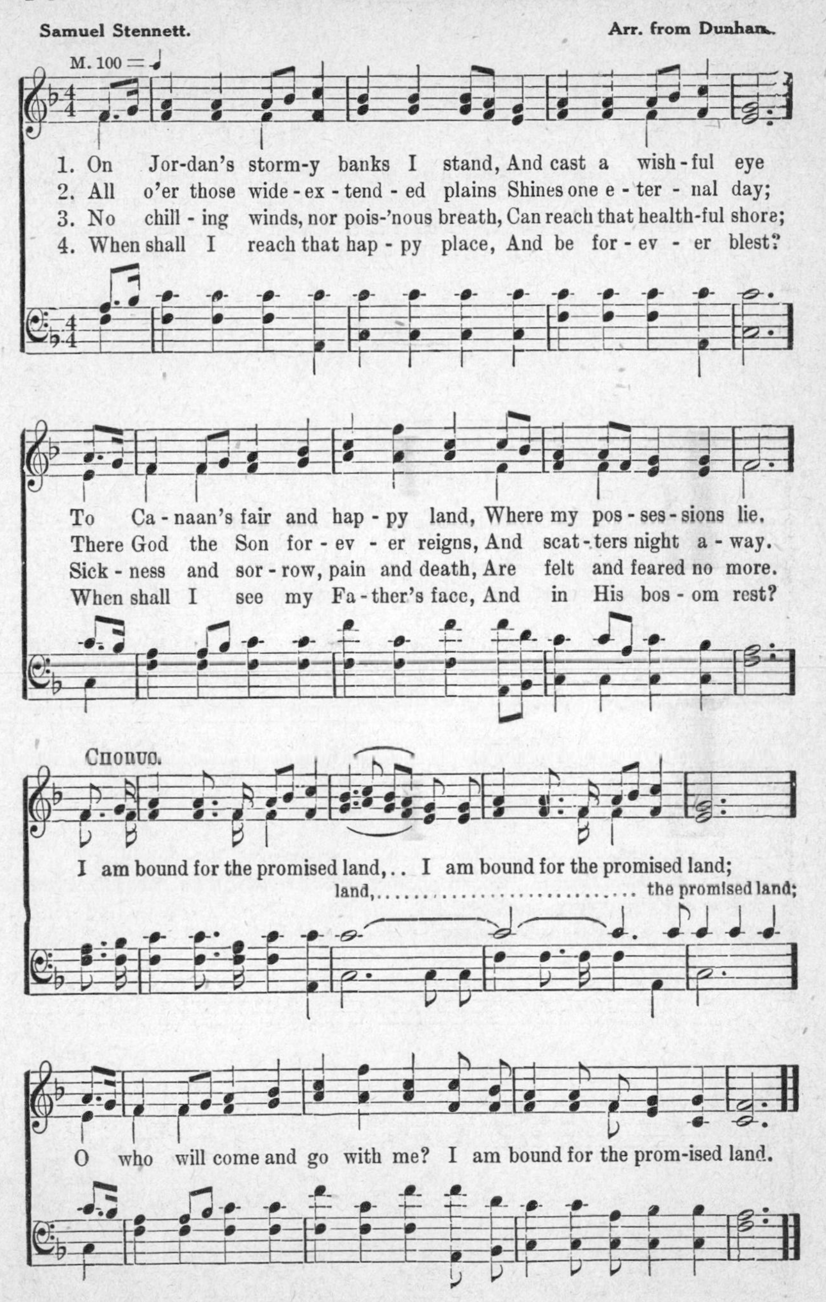
M. 100 = ♩
1. On Jor-dan's storm-y banks I stand, And cast a wish-ful eye
2. All o'er those wide-ex-tend-ed plains Shines one e-ter-nal day;
3. No chill-ing winds, nor pois-'nous breath, Can reach that health-ful shore;
4. When shall I reach that hap-py place, And be for-ev-er blest?
To Ca-naan's fair and hap-py land, Where my pos-ses-sions lie.
There God the Son for-ev-er reigns, And scat-ters night a-way.
Sick-ness and sor-row, pain and death, Are felt and feared no more.
When shall I see my Fa-ther's face, And in His bos-om rest?
Chorus.
I am bound for the promised land,.. I am bound for the promised land;
land,............................ the promised land;
O who will come and go with me? I am bound for the prom-ised land.

74.
Only One Way.
COPYRIGHT, 1912 BY CHAS. H. GABRIEL.
HOMER A. RODEHEAVER, OWNER.
E. E. Rexford.
Chas. H. Gabriel.
1. There is on - ly one way of sal - va-tion—The glo-ri-ous way of the cross!
2. There is on - ly one way of sal - va-tion! At Cal-va-ry's cross it be - gins,
3. There is on - ly one way of sal - va-tion, Tho' oft-en it seems to be vain—
It leads thro' Gethsemane's gar-den, Thro'pain,self-de-ni-al and loss.
And winds thro'the vale of re - pent-ance, And out of the val-ley of sins.
It's mountains of tri - al and sor - row, It's des-erts of pas-sion and pain—
'Tis nar-row, but ev - er a-bound-ing With glimpses of heav-en a - bove;
'Tis marked by the blood of the martyrs, And hallowed by sor-rows un - told,
But Je - sus, the Sav-ior of sin - ners, Will walk by your side all the way;
FINE
It is rug-ged, but ra-diant with glo - ry, And blazoned with mer-cy and love.
But it still is the way, and the on - ly Way un - to the Cit - y of Gold.
He will guide you, and cheer you, and love you—O make Him your Savior to-day.
D.S.—There is on - ly one way of sal - va - tion, The glo - ri-ous way of the cross.
Chorus.
D. S.
There is on - ly one way of sal-va - tion—The way. . . . . . of the cross; . . . .
One way, ... one way—The glo-ri-ous way. . . . . of the cross;

75. I Shall See the King.

Rev. W. C. Poole.

B. D. Ackley.

M. 92 = ♩
1. I shall see the King Where the an - gels sing, I shall see the King some day, In the bet - ter land, On the gold - en strand, And with Him shall ev - er stay.
2. In the land of song, In the glo - ry-throng, Where there nev - er comes a night, With my Lord once slain I shall ev - er reign In the glo - ry land of light.
3. I shall see the King, All my trib - utes bring, And shall look up- on His face; Then my song shall be How He ran-somed me And has kept me by His grace.
CHORUS.
In His glo - ry, I shall see the King, And for - ev - er end - less prais - es sing; 'Twas on Cal - va - ry Je - sus died for me; I shall see the King some day.

76. How Tedious and Tasteless.
John Newton.
German.
M. 54 = ♩.
1. How ted-ious and tasteless the hours When Je-sus no lon-ger I see;
2. His name yields the rich-est per-fume, And sweet-er than mu-sic His voice;
FINE.
Sweet prospects, sweet birds, and sweet flow'rs, Have all lost their sweetness to me;
His pres-ence dis-pers-es my gloom, And makes all with-in me re-joice;
D.S.-But when I am hap-py in Him, De-cem-ber's as pleas-ant as May.
D.S.-No mor-tal so hap-py as I, My sum-mer would last all the year.
D.S.
The mid-sum-mer sun shines but dim, The fields strive in vain to look gay;
I should, were He al-ways thus nigh, Have noth-ing to wish or to fear;
3 Content with beholding His face,
My all to His pleasure resigned,
No changes of season or place
Would make any change in my mind:
While blest with a sense of His love,
A palace a toy would appear;
And prisons would palaces prove,
If Jesus would dwell with me there.
4 Dear Lord, if indeed I am Thine,
If Thou art my sun and my song,
Say, why do I languish and pine?
And why are my winters so long?
O drive these dark clouds from the sky,
Thy soul-cheering presence restore;
Or take me to Thee up on high,
Where winter and clouds are no more.
77. Faith of Our Fathers!
Frederick W. Faber.
Arr. by J. G. Walton.
M. 120 = ♩
1. Faith of our fa-thers! liv-ing still In spite of dun-geon, fire, and sword:
2. Our fa-thers, chained in pris-ons dark, Were still in heart and conscience free:
3. Faith of our fa-thers! we will love Both friend and foe in all our strife:

Faith of Our Fathers.

O how our hearts beat high with joy Whene'er we hear that glo-rious word!
How sweet would be their children's fate, If they, like them, could die for thee!
And preach thee, too, as love knows how, By kind-ly words and vir - tuous life:
Faith of our fa-thers! ho - ly faith! We will be true to thee till death!
78.
Just As I Am.
Charlotte Elliott.
Wm. B. Bradbury.
1. Just as I am, with - out one plea, But that Thy blood was shed for me,
2. Just as I am, and wait - ing not To rid my soul of one dark blot,
3. Just as I am, tho' tossed a-bout With ma - ny a conflict, many a doubt,
4. Just as I am, poor, wretched, blind, Sight, rich-es, heal-ing of the mind,
5. Just as I am, Thou wilt re-ceive, Wilt welcome, par-don, cleanse, relieve;
6. Just as I am, Thy love un-known Hath brok-en ev - 'ry bar-rier down;
And that Thou bidd'st me come to Thee, O Lamb of God, I come! I come!
To Thee, whose blood can cleanse each spot, O Lamb of God, I come! I come!
Fight - ings with-in, and fears with-out, O Lamb of God, I come! I come!
Yea, all I need, in Thee to find, O Lamb of God, I come! I come!
Be - cause Thy prom-ise I be-lieve, O Lamb of God, I come! I come!
Now, to be Thine, yea, Thine a - lone, O Lamb of God, I come! I come!

79. Pentecostal Power.

COPYRIGHT, 1912, BY CHAS. H. GABRIEL.
HOMER A. RODEHEAVER, OWNER.
Charlotte G. Homer
Chas. H. Gabriel.
M. 108 =
1. Lord, as of old at Pen - te - cost Thou didst Thy pow'r dis - play,
2. For might-y works for Thee pre-pare, And strengthen ev - 'ry heart;
3. All self con-sume, all sin de-stroy! With ear - nest zeal en - due
4. Speak, Lord! be - fore Thy throne we wait, Thy prom - ise we be - lieve,
With cleans-ing, pu - ri - fy - ing flame De - scend on us to - day.
Come, take pos - ses - sion of Thine own, And nev - er - more de - part.
Each wait - ing heart to work for Thee; O Lord, our faith re - new!
And will not let Thee go un - til The bless-ing we re - ceive.
CHORUS.
Lord, send the old-time pow'r, The Pen - te - cos - tal pow'r! Thy flood-gates of
bless-ing on us throw o - pen wide! Lord, send the old - time pow'r, the
Pen-te-cos-tal pow'r, That sinners be con-vert-ed and Thy name glo-ri - fied!

80.

God Will Take Care of You.

Dedicated to my wife, Mrs. John A. Davis.

C. D. Martin.
W. S. Martin.
M. 54 = ♩.
1. Be not dis-mayed what-e'er be - tide, God will take care of you;
2. Thro' days of toil when heart doth fail, God will take care of you;
3. All you may need He will pro-vide, God will take care of you;
4. No mat-ter what may be the test, God will take care of you;
Be-neath His wings of love a - bide, God will take care of you.
When dan-gers fierce your path as - sail, God will take care of you.
Noth-ing you ask will be de - nied, God will take care of you.
Lean, wea-ry one, up - on His breast, God will take care of you.
Chorus.
God will take care of you, Thro' ev - 'ry day, O'er all the way;
He will take care of you, God will take care of you.........
take care of you.

81 My Faith Looks Up to Thee.

Ray Palmer. Lowell Mason.

M. 48 = 𝅗𝅥
1. My faith looks up to Thee, Thou Lamb of Cal-va-ry, Sav-ior di-vine! Now hear me
2. May Thy rich grace impart Strength to my fainting heart, My zeal in-spire; As Thou hast
3. While life's dark maze I tread, And griefs around me spread, Be Thou my Guide; Bid darkness
while I pray, Take all my guilt a-way, O let me from this day Be whol-ly Thine!
died for me, O may my love to Thee Pure, warm, and changeless be, A liv-ing fire!
turn to day, Wipe sorrow's tears away, Nor let me ever stray From Thee a-side.

82 Rock of Ages.

A. M. Toplady. Thomas Hastings.

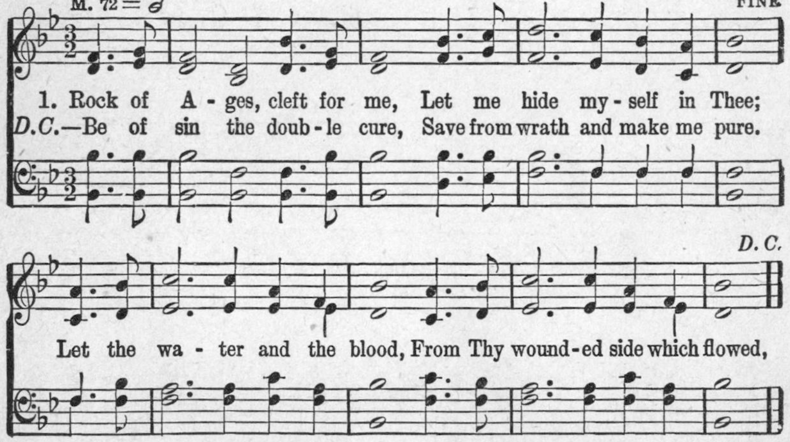
M. 72 = 𝅗𝅥
FINE
1. Rock of A - ges, cleft for me, Let me hide my - self in Thee;
D.C.—Be of sin the doub - le cure, Save from wrath and make me pure.
D. C.
Let the wa - ter and the blood, From Thy wound - ed side which flowed,

2 Could my tears forever flow,
Could my zeal no languor know,
These for sin could not atone;
Thou must save, and Thou alone:
In my hand no price I bring;
Simply to Thy cross I cling.

3 While I draw this fleeting breath,
When my eyes shall close in death,
When I rise to worlds unknown,
And behold Thee on Thy throne,
Rock of Ages, cleft for me,
Let me hide myself in Thee.

Invitation Hymns

83.

Jesus is Calling.

Fanny J. Crosby.

George C. Stebbins.

1. Je-sus is ten-der-ly call-ing thee home—Call-ing to-day, call-ing to-day;
2. Je-sus is call-ing the wea-ry to rest— Call-ing to-day, call-ing to-day;
3. Je-sus is wait-ing, O come to Him now—Wait-ing to-day, wait-ing to-day;
4. Je-sus is plead-ing, O list to His voice—Hear Him to-day, hear Him to-day;
Why from the sun-shine of love wilt thou roam Far-ther and far-ther a - way?
Bring Him thy burden, and thou shalt be blest; He will not turn thee a - way.
Come with thy sins, at His feet low - ly bow; Come, and no long - er de - lay.
They who be-lieve on His name shall re-joice; Quick-ly a - rise and a - way.
CHORUS.
Call - - ing to - day!....... Call - - ing to - day!......
Call - ing, call - ing to - day, to - day! Call - ing, call - ing to - day, to - day!
Je - - sus is call - - - ing, is ten - der-ly call-ing to - day.
Je - sus is ten - der - ly call - ing to - day,

84.
I Am Resolved.
Palmer Hartsough.
COPYRIGHT, 1896, BY FILLMORE BROS.
J. A. LEE, OWNER.
J. H. Fillmore.
M. 100 = ♩
1. I am re-solved no lon - ger to lin - ger, Charmed by the
2. I am re-solved to go to the Sav - ior, Leav - ing my
3. I am re-solved to fol - low the Sav - ior, Faith - ful and
4. I am re-solved to en - ter the king - dom, Leav - ing the
5. I am re-solved, and who will go with me? Come, friends, with-
world's de - light; Things that are high - er, things that are no - bler,
sin and strife; He is the true One, He is the just One,
true each day, Heed what He say - eth, do what He will - eth,
paths of sin; Friends may op- - pose me, foes may be - set me,
out de - lay, Taught by the Bi - ble, led by the Spir - it,
CHORUS.
These have al - lured my sight.
He hath the words of life.
He is the liv - ing way.
Still will I en - ter in.
We'll walk the heav-'nly way.
I will hast - en to Him
I will hast-en, hast - en to Him,
Hast - en so glad and free, (Hast - en glad and free),
Je - sus, great - est, high - est, I will come to Thee.
Je - sus, Je - sus,

85.

Still Undecided.

Ernest G. Wesley. Chas. H. Gabriel.

M. 69 = 𝅗𝅥.
1. Still un-de-cid-ed, tho' close to life's gate, O why not now
2. Still un-de-cid-ed, why yet still de-lay? All things are now
3. Still un-de-cid-ed! for thee He was slain, And why should His
4. Still un-de-cid-ed! His voice sounds so clear: "Come all ye who
5. Still un-de-cid-ed! O wait not too long; O turn from the
en-ter, al-read-y 'tis late; Je-sus is wait-ing and call-ing for you;
read-y, Love shows you the way, Night fast approaches, the day pass-es by,
suf-f'ring for thee be in vain? Think of the scourging, the spear and the cross!
wea-ry who fal-ter and fear, Free-ly I par-don, and cleanse and receive!"
world and its wild, restless throng; Je-sus now calls you–once more doth He call–
Chains He will sev-er– all things He can do.
Heed now His plead-ing:–"O why will you die?"
Life He would give you,–all else is but loss.
Why not ac-cept Him and on Him be-lieve?
Come while He's wait-ing, and trust Him for all.
CHORUS.
Why not de-cide to-night?
Why not de-cide to-night? Je-sus is wait-ing and call-ing for thee,
1
Call-ing for thee, call-ing for thee; Call-ing, is call-ing now for thee.
2

86.
Pass Me Not.
Fanny J. Crosby.
USED BY PERMISSION.
W. H. Doane.
M. 76 = ♩
1. Pass me not, O gen-tle Sav-ior, Hear my hum-ble cry; While on oth-ers Thou art call-ing, Do not pass me by.
2. Let me at a throne of mer-cy Find a sweet re-lief; Kneel-ing there in deep con-tri-tion, Help my un-be-lief.
3. Trust-ing on-ly in Thy mer-it, Would I seek Thy face; Heal my wound-ed, bro-ken spir-it, Save me by Thy grace.
4. Thou the Spring of all my com-fort, More than life to me, Whom have I on earth be-side Thee? Whom in heav'n but Thee?
FINE. CHORUS.
Sav-ior, Sav-ior, Hear my hum-ble cry;
D. S.
87.
Where He Leads Me.
E. W. Blandly.
J. S. Norris.
M. 88 = ♩
1. I can hear my Sav-ior call-ing, I can hear my Sav-ior call-ing, I can hear my Sav-ior call-ing, "Take thy cross and fol-low, fol-low Me."
2. I'll go with Him thro' the gar-den, I'll go with Him thro' the gar-den, I'll go with Him thro' the gar-den, I'll go with Him, with Him all the way.
3. I'll go with Him thro' the judg-ment, I'll go with Him thro' the judg-ment, I'll go with Him thro' the judgment, I'll go with Him, with Him all the way.
4. He will give me grace and glo-ry, He will give me grace and glo-ry, He will give me grace and glo-ry, And go with me, with me all the way.
D.C.-Where He leads me I will fol-low, Where He leads me I will fol-low,
D. C.
Where He leads me I will fol-low, I'll go with Him, with Him all the way.

88. Why Not Now?

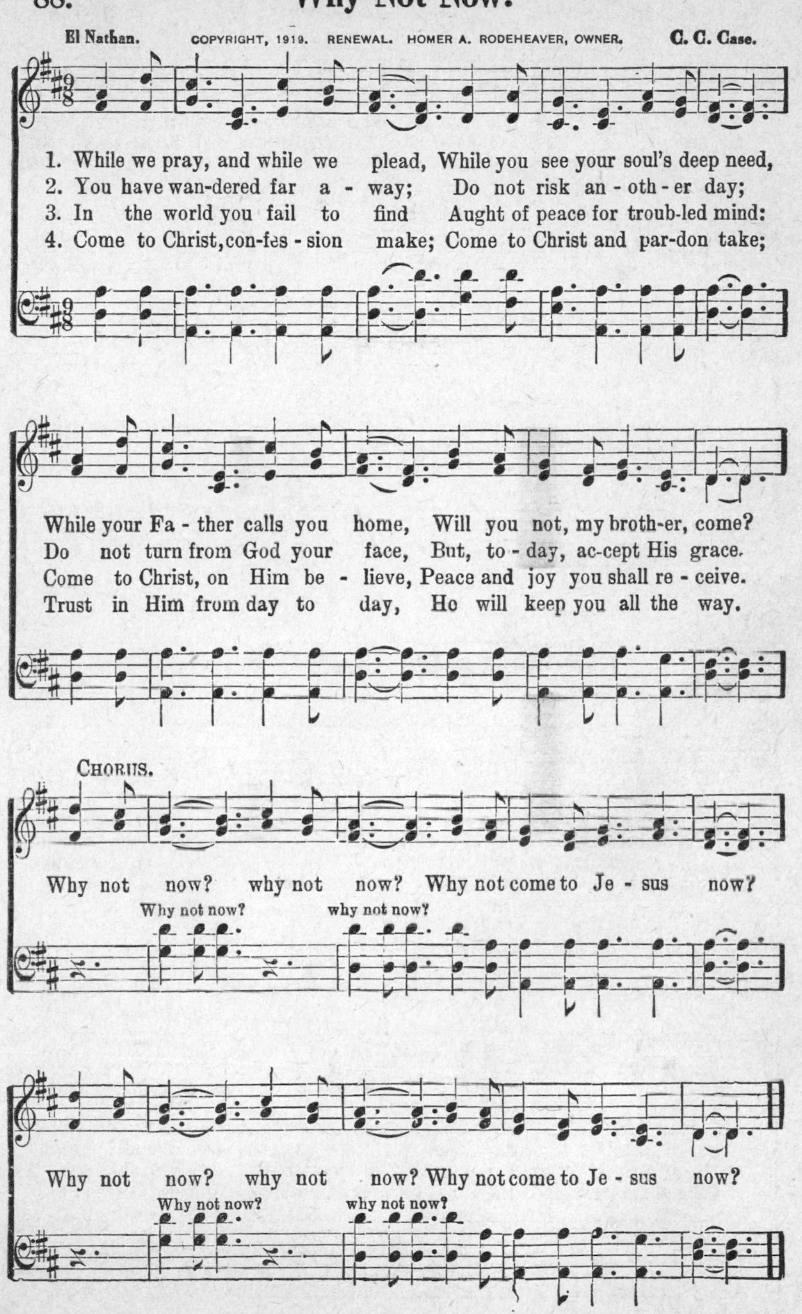
El Nathan.
COPYRIGHT, 1919. RENEWAL. HOMER A. RODEHEAVER, OWNER.
C. C. Case.
1. While we pray, and while we plead, While you see your soul's deep need,
2. You have wan-dered far a - way; Do not risk an - oth - er day;
3. In the world you fail to find Aught of peace for troub-led mind:
4. Come to Christ, con-fes - sion make; Come to Christ and par-don take;
While your Fa - ther calls you home, Will you not, my broth-er, come?
Do not turn from God your face, But, to - day, ac-cept His grace.
Come to Christ, on Him be - lieve, Peace and joy you shall re - ceive.
Trust in Him from day to day, He will keep you all the way.
CHORUS.
Why not now? why not now? Why not come to Je - sus now?
Why not now? why not now?
Why not now? why not now? Why not come to Je - sus now?
Why not now? why not now?

89 Lord, I'm Coming Home.
W. J. K.
COPYRIGHT, 1892, BY WM. J. KIRKPATRICK.
Wm. J. Kirkpatrick.
1. I've wan-dered far a - way from God, Now I'm com-ing home;
2. I've wast - ed man - y pre - cious years, Now I'm com-ing home;
3. I'm tired of sin and stray - ing, Lord, Now I'm com-ing home;
4. My soul is sick, my heart is sore, Now I'm com-ing home;
FINE.
The paths of sin too long I've trod, Lord, I'm com-ing home.
I now re - pent with bit - ter tears, Lord, I'm com-ing home.
I'll trust Thy love, be - lieve Thy word, Lord, I'm com-ing home.
My strength re - new, my hope re - store, Lord, I'm com-ing home.
D. S.—O - pen wide Thine arms of love, Lord, I'm com-ing home.
CHORUS.
D. S.
Com - ing home, com - ing home, Nev - er more to roam;
90. Come to Jesus.
M. 84 = ♩
1. Come to Je - sus, come to Je - sus, Come to Je - sus just now, Just now,
2. He will save you, He will save you, He will save you just now, Just now,
Come to Je - sus, come to Je - sus just now.
He will save you, He will save you just now.
4. He is able.
5. He is willing.
6. Call upon Him.
7. He will hear you.
8. He'll forgive you.
9. He will cleanse you.
10. Jesus loves you.
11. Only trust Him.

91. I Am Coming Home.

A. H. Ackley. B. D. Ackley.

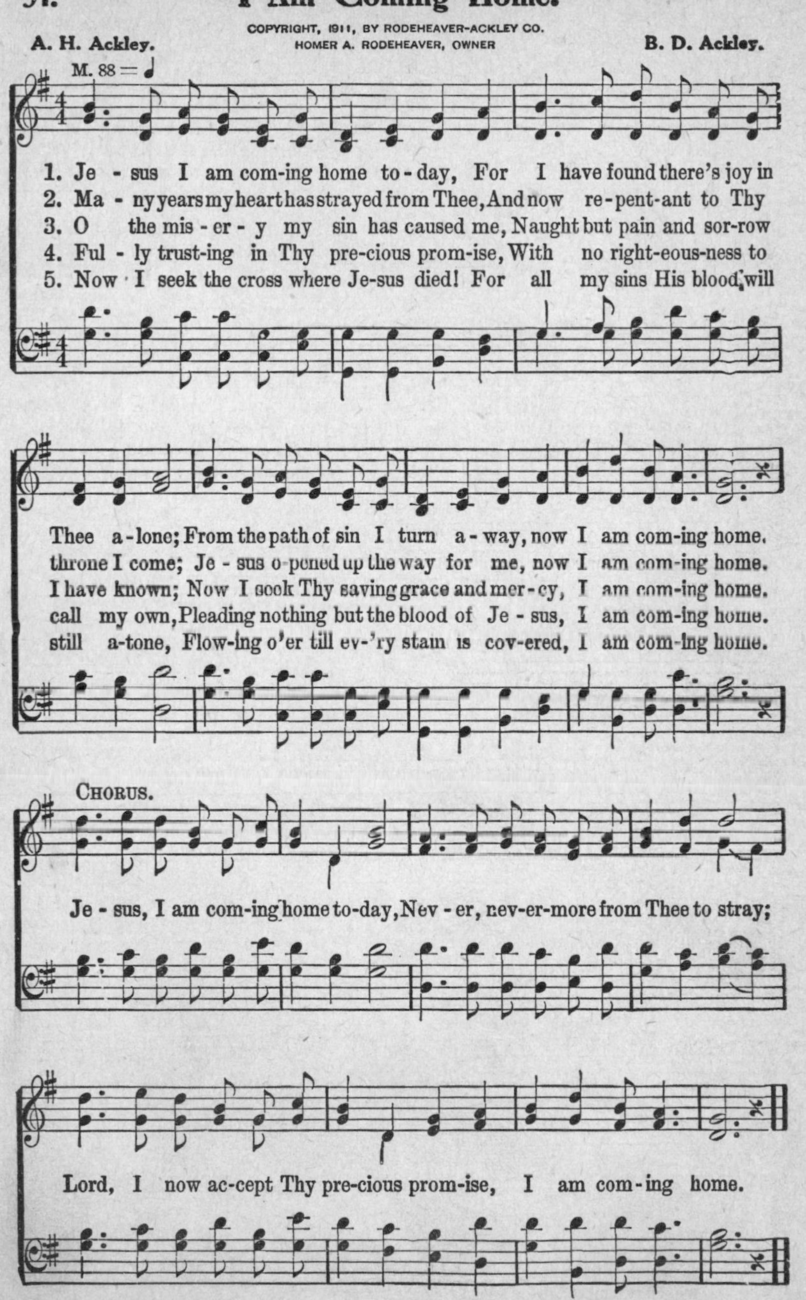
M. 88 = ♩
1. Je - sus I am com-ing home to - day, For I have found there's joy in
2. Ma - ny years my heart has strayed from Thee, And now re-pent-ant to Thy
3. O the mis - er - y my sin has caused me, Naught but pain and sor-row
4. Ful - ly trust-ing in Thy pre-cious prom-ise, With no right-eous-ness to
5. Now I seek the cross where Je-sus died! For all my sins His blood will
Thee a-lone; From the path of sin I turn a - way, now I am com-ing home.
throne I come; Je - sus o-pened up the way for me, now I am com-ing home.
I have known; Now I seek Thy saving grace and mer - cy, I am com-ing home.
call my own, Pleading nothing but the blood of Je - sus, I am com-ing home.
still a-tone, Flow-ing o'er till ev-'ry stain is cov-ered, I am com-ing home.
CHORUS.
Je - sus, I am com-ing home to-day, Nev - er, nev-er-more from Thee to stray;
Lord, I now ac-cept Thy pre-cious prom-ise, I am com - ing home.

92. He is Knocking.

E. E. Hewitt. B. D. Ackley.

M. 84 =
1. He is knock-ing, soft-ly knocking at the door; Let Him in,............
2. He is call-ing, gen-tly call-ing to you now; Let Him in,............
3. He is wait-ing, kind-ly wait-ing still for you; Let Him in,............
O let Him in,
O let Him in; He will bring you rich-est blessing ev - er - more;
O let Him in; See the plead-ing dews of mer-cy on His brow;
O let Him in; Give Him welcome, joyful welcome, warm and true;
O let Him in;
Let Him in,.......... O let Him in!
O let Him in, O let Him in!
CHORUS.
Knock-ing, knock-ing!
O-pen wide the door, Let Him in to-day, Ask Him in to stay;
O let Him in, Ask Him in, He's
Knocking, knocking! life He will re-store, When you open wide the door.....
bolt-ed door.

93. Softly and Tenderly.
HOPE PUBLISHING CO., OWNER.
USED BY PERMISSION.
W. L. T.
Will L. Thompson.
pp
m
1. Soft - ly and ten-der - ly Je-sus is call-ing, Call-ing for you and for me;
2. Why should we tarry when Je-sus is plead-ing, Plead-ing for you and for me?
3. Time is now fleeting, the moments are pass-ing, Pass-ing from you and from me;
4. Think of the won-der-ful love He has promised, Promised for you and for me;
At the heart's por-tal He's waiting and watching, Watching for you and for me.
Why should we lin-ger and heed not His mercies, Mer-cies for you and for me?
Shadows are gath'ring,and death's night is coming, Com-ing for you and for me.
Tho' we have sinn'd, He has mer-cy and par-don, Par-don for you and for me.
CHORUS.
cres.
Come home, come home, Ye who are wea-ry, come home,
Come home, come home,
p
rit.
pp
Ear-nest-ly, ten-der - ly, Je-sus is call-ing, Call-ing, O sin-ner, come home!
94. While Jesus Whispers.
COPYRIGHT, 1879, BY H. R. PALMER
USED BY PERMISSION.
W. E. Witter.
H. R. Palmer
1. While Je-sus whispers to you, Come, sinner, come! While we are praying for you, Come, sinner, come!
2. Are you too heav-y - la-den? Come, sinner, come! Jesus will bear your burden, Come, sinner, come!
3. O hear His tender pleading, Come, sinner, come! Come and receive the blessing, Come, sinner, come!
Now is the time to own Him, Come, sinner, come! Now is the time to know Him, Come, sinner, come!
Je - sus will not deceive you, Come, sinner, come! Je - sus can now redeem you, Come, sinner, come!
While Je-sus whispers to you, Come, sinner, come! While we are praying for you, Come, sinner, come!

95. "Almost Persuaded."
P. P. B.
Copyright, 1902, by The John Church Co.
P. P. Bliss.
M. 152 = ♪
1. "Al - most per-suad - ed" now to be - lieve; "Al - most per - suad - ed" Christ to re - ceive; Seems now some soul to say: "Go, Spir - it, go Thy way, Some more con - ven - ient day On Thee I'll call."
2. "Al - most per-suad - ed"—come, come to - day! "Al - most per - suad - ed" turn not a - way! Je - sus in - vites you here, An - gels are lin-g'ring near, Pray'rs rise from hearts so dear; O wan - d'rer, come!
3. "Al - most per-suad - ed"—har-vest is past! "Al - most per - suad - ed" doom comes at last! "Al - most" can - not a - vail, "Al - most" is but to fail; Sad, sad, that bit - ter wail; "Al - most—but lost!"
96. I'll Live For Him.
R. E. Hudson.
Used by permission.
C. R. Dunbar.
M. 166 = ♩
1. My life, my love I give to Thee, Thou Lamb of God, who died for me; O may I ev - er faith - ful be, My Sav - ior and my God!
2. I now be-lieve Thou dost re-ceive, For Thou hast died that I might live; And now hence-forth I'll trust in Thee, My Sav - ior and my God!
2- O Thou who died on Cal - va - ry To save my soul and make me free, I con - se - crate my life to Thee, My Sav - ior and my God!
Cho.—I'll live for Him who died for me, How hap - py then my life shall be! I'll live for Him who died for me, My Sav - ior and my God!

Children's Songs

97. Jesus Loves Even Me.

P. P. B. P. P. Bliss.

1. I am so glad that our Father in heav'n
Tells of His love in the Book He has giv'n;
Wonderful things in the Bible I see,
This is the dearest, that Jesus loves me.

2. Tho' I forget Him and wander away,
Still He doth love me wher-ever I stray;
Back to His dear loving arms would I flee,
When I remember that Jesus loves me.

3. Oh, if there's only one song I can sing,
When in His beauty I see the Great King,
This shall my song in eternity be:
"Oh, what a wonder that Jesus loves me.

CHORUS.

I am so glad that Jesus loves me, Jesus loves me, Jesus loves me;
I am so glad that Jesus loves me, Jesus loves even me.

98. The Heavenly Stranger.

Ada Blenkhorn. Chas. H. Gabriel.

1 No warm, down-y pil-low His sweet head pressed, No soft silk-en garments His
2. No jub-i-lant clang of re-joic-ing bell The glo-ri-ous news to the
3. All hail to Thee, Je-sus, Thou Ho-ly One! All hail to Thee, Je-sus! Je-
fair form dressed; He lay in a man-ger, this heav-en-ly Stranger, The
world did tell; But an-gels from glo-ry sang sweet-ly the sto-ry Of
ho-vah's Son; While an-gels a-dore Thee, we'll wor-ship be-fore Thee, Our
precious Lord Je-sus, the won-der-ful Child.
Bethlehem's Stranger, the Sav-ior of men.
bless-ed Mes-si-ah, our Sav-ior and King.
CHORUS. (with Violin Ob.)
Thou heav-en-ly Stran-ger so gen-tle and mild,
We'll wor-ship be-fore Thee, and praise and a-dore Thee,
1
Tho' born in a man-ger, the Father's own child;
2
And sing the glad sto-ry a-gain and a-gain.

99. Swing Song.

Edith Sanford Tillotson. B. D. Ackley.

1. Who wants to travel to Tree Top Land? Who wants to ride with a jol - ly band?
2. Who wants to see where the Robin lives? Who wants the pleasure that flying gives?
3. Who wants to peep into Cloudland bright? Who wants to follow the sunbeams' light?
Who likes to rise like a bird on the wing? Come and we'll go in the swing!
Who loves to hear what the soft breezes sing! Come then with us in the swing!
Come then, the fare is the song that we bring, Come take a trip in the swing!
CHORUS.
Off we go— to and fro, Swinging, swinging, swing - ing; O what fun—
swing-ing, swing ing,
ev-'ry one, Singing, singing, sing-ing; Merry lay—laughter gay, Ringing, ringing,
ring - ing; Light and free as the birds are we! O, the joy of swing-ing!
ring - ing, ring-ing,

100. Spelling Love.

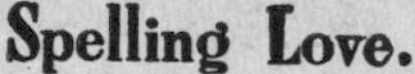

Lucia B. Cook. | Chas. H. Gabriel.

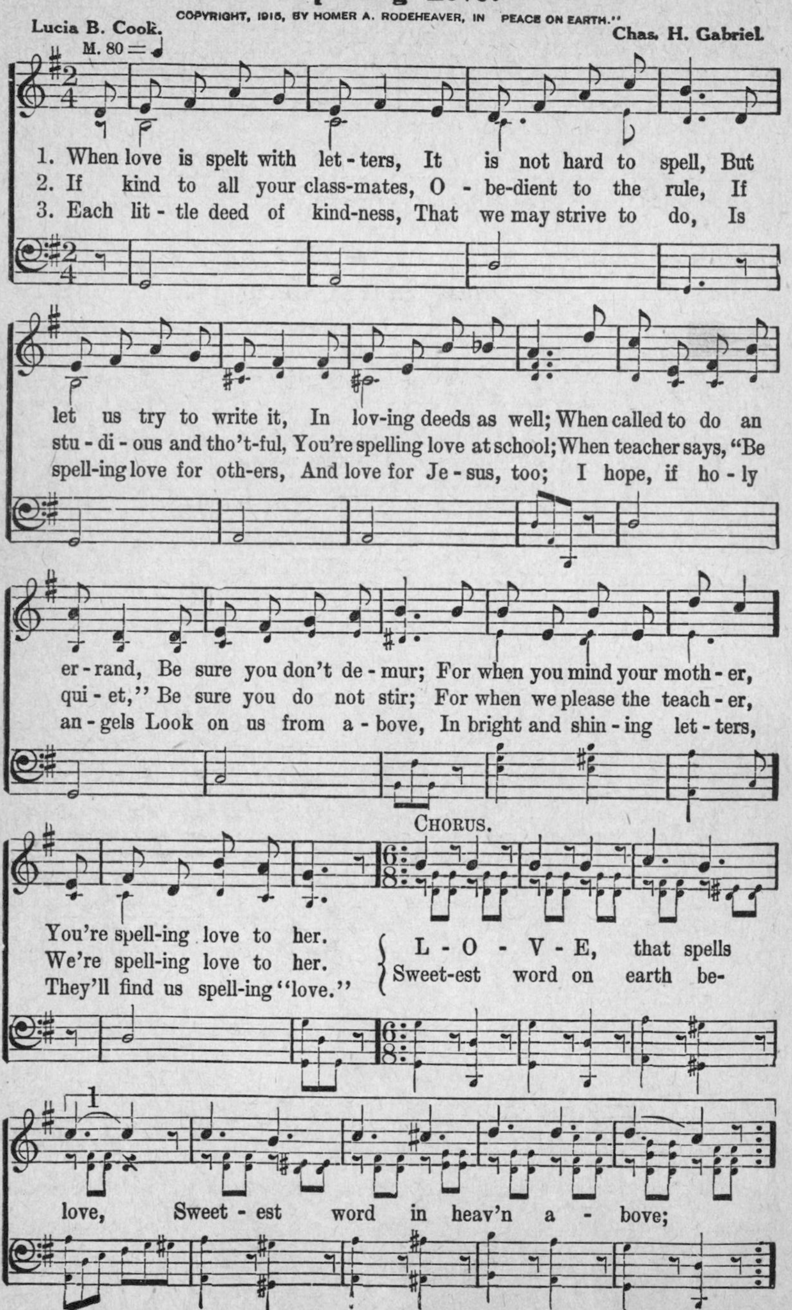
M. 80 = ♩
1. When love is spelt with let-ters, It is not hard to spell, But
2. If kind to all your class-mates, O-be-dient to the rule, If
3. Each lit-tle deed of kind-ness, That we may strive to do, Is
let us try to write it, In lov-ing deeds as well; When called to do an
stu-di-ous and tho't-ful, You're spelling love at school; When teacher says, "Be
spell-ing love for oth-ers, And love for Je-sus, too; I hope, if ho-ly
er-rand, Be sure you don't de-mur; For when you mind your moth-er,
qui-et," Be sure you do not stir; For when we please the teach-er,
an-gels Look on us from a-bove, In bright and shin-ing let-ters,
You're spell-ing love to her.
We're spell-ing love to her.
They'll find us spell-ing "love."
CHORUS.
L-O-V-E, that spells
Sweet-est word on earth be-
love,
Sweet-est word in heav'n a-bove;

Spelling Love.
low,..... Let's keep spell - ing as we go.......
101. Jesus Loves Me.
Wm. B. Bradbury.
1. Je - sus loves me! this I know, For the Bi - ble tells me so;
2. Je - sus loves me! He who died, Heav-en's gate to o - pen wide,
3. Je - sus loves me, loves me still, Tho' I'm ver - y weak and ill;
4. Je - sus loves me! He will stay Close be - side me all the way;
Lit - tle ones to Him be - long, They are weak but He is strong.
He will wash a - way my sin, Let His lit - tle child come in.
From His shin-ing throne on high, Comes to watch me where I lie.
If I love Him when I die, He will take me home on high.
Chorus.
Yes, Jesus loves me, Yes, Jesus loves me, Yes, Jesus loves me, The bible tells me so.

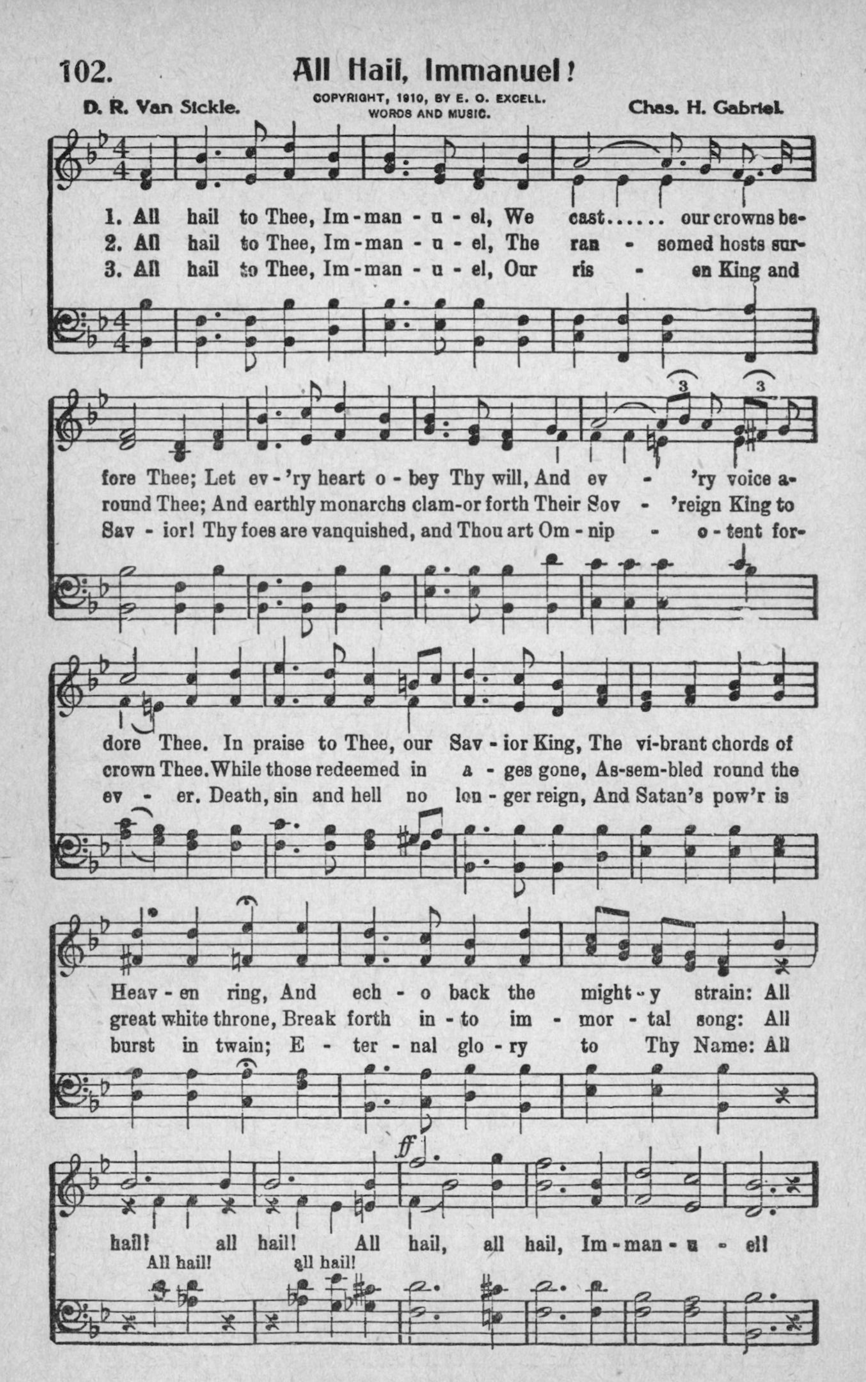
102. All Hail, Immanuel!
COPYRIGHT, 1910, BY E. O. EXCELL. WORDS AND MUSIC.
D. R. Van Sickle.
Chas. H. Gabriel.
1. All hail to Thee, Im-man-u-el, We cast...... our crowns be-
2. All hail to Thee, Im-man-u-el, The ran - somed hosts sur-
3. All hail to Thee, Im-man-u-el, Our ris - en King and
fore Thee; Let ev-'ry heart o-bey Thy will, And ev - 'ry voice a-
round Thee; And earthly monarchs clam-or forth Their Sov - 'reign King to
Sav - ior! Thy foes are vanquished, and Thou art Om-nip - o-tent for-
dore Thee. In praise to Thee, our Sav-ior King, The vi-brant chords of
crown Thee. While those redeemed in a-ges gone, As-sem-bled round the
ev - er. Death, sin and hell no lon-ger reign, And Satan's pow'r is
Heav-en ring, And ech-o back the might-y strain: All
great white throne, Break forth in-to im - mor-tal song: All
burst in twain; E - ter-nal glo-ry to Thy Name: All
hail! all hail! All hail, all hail, Im-man-u-el!
All hail! all hail!
ff

All Hail, Immanuel!
Chorus.
Hail,.............. Im-man-u-el! Im-man-u-el! Hail,.............
Hail to the King we love so well, Hail, Im - man-u-el! Hail to the King we love so well,
Hail!.... ....
Im-man-u-el, Im-man-u-el!
Hail, Im - man-u-el! Glory and honor and majesty, Wisdom and power be
Hail!...... .... Glo - ry and maj-es-ty, Wis - dom be
rit. - - - - - - - Hail,.................. Im-
un - to Thee, Now and ev - er - more! Hail to the King we love so well,
man-u-el, Im-man-u-el! Hail,.............. Im-man-u-el, Im-man-u-el!
Hail, Im - man - u - el! Hail to the King we love so well, Hail, Im - man - u-el!
Hail! .... Hail! ....
King of kings and Lord of lords, All hail, Im-man - u - el!

103. Awakening Chorus.

Charlotte G. Homer.
Chas. H. Gabriel.
M. 76 =
1. A- wake! a - wake! and sing the bless - ed sto - ry; A-
A-wake! a - wake!
2. Ring out! ring out! O bells of joy and glad - ness! Re-
Ring out! ring out!
wake! a - wake! and let your song of praise a-rise; A-wake! a-
A - wake! a-wake! a - wake!
peat, re - peat a - new the sto - ry o'er a-gain, Till all the
Re - peat. re - peat Till all
wake! the earth is full of glo - ry, And light is beam - ing
a - wake! And light is beam-ing
earth shall lose its weight of sad-ness, And shout a - new the
the earth And shout a - new
Male voices in Unison.
from the ra-diant skies; The rocks and rills, the vales and hills resound with
glo - ri - ous re - frain; With an-gels in the heights sing of the great sal-
Full harmony.
glad - ness, All na - ture joins to sing the tri-umph song. The Lord Je-
va - tion He wrest - ed from the hand of sin and death.

Awakening Chorus.
Unison.
ho - vah reigns and sin is back-ward hurled! Re-joice! re-
is sin backward hurled!
joice! lift heart and voice, Je - ho - vah reigns!
Full harmony.
Pro-claim His sov-'reign pow'r to all the world, And let His
pow'r to all the world, And let the
glo - rious ban-ner be un-furled! Je - ho - vah reigns!
grand and glo-rious ban-ner be un-furled! Je - ho - vah reigns! Je - ho - vah reigns!
Re - joice! re - joice! re - joice! Je - ho - vah reigns!
Re - joice! re - joice! re - joice!

104 Master, the Tempest is Raging.
USED BY PER OF H R PALMER.
OWNER O. COPYRIGHT.
Miss M. A. Baker.
H. R. Palmer.
M. 69 = ♩.
1. Mas - ter, the tem - pest is rag - ing! The bil - lows are toss - ing high!
2. Mas - ter, with an - guish of spir - it I bow in my grief to - day;
3. Mas - ter, the ter - ror is o - ver, The el - e-ments sweet - ly rest;
The sky is o'er-shadowed with blackness, No shel - ter or help is nigh;
The depths of my sad heart are troub - led—O wak - en and save, I pray;
Earth's sun in the calm lake is mir-rored, And heaven's with-in my breast;
Car - est Thou not that we per - ish? How canst Thou lie a - sleep,
Tor - rents of sin and of an - guish Sweep o'er my sink - ing soul;
Lin - ger, O bless - ed Re-deem - er! Leave me a - lone no more,
When each mo-ment so mad - ly is threat'ning A grave in the an - gry deep?
And I per - ish! I per - ish! dear Mas - ter, O has - ten and take con - trol.
And with joy I shall make the blest har - bor, And rest on the bliss - ful shore.
CHORUS.
p
pp
The winds and the waves shall o - bey Thy will, Peace, ... be still! .....
Peace, be still, peace, be still!

Master, the Tempest is Raging.

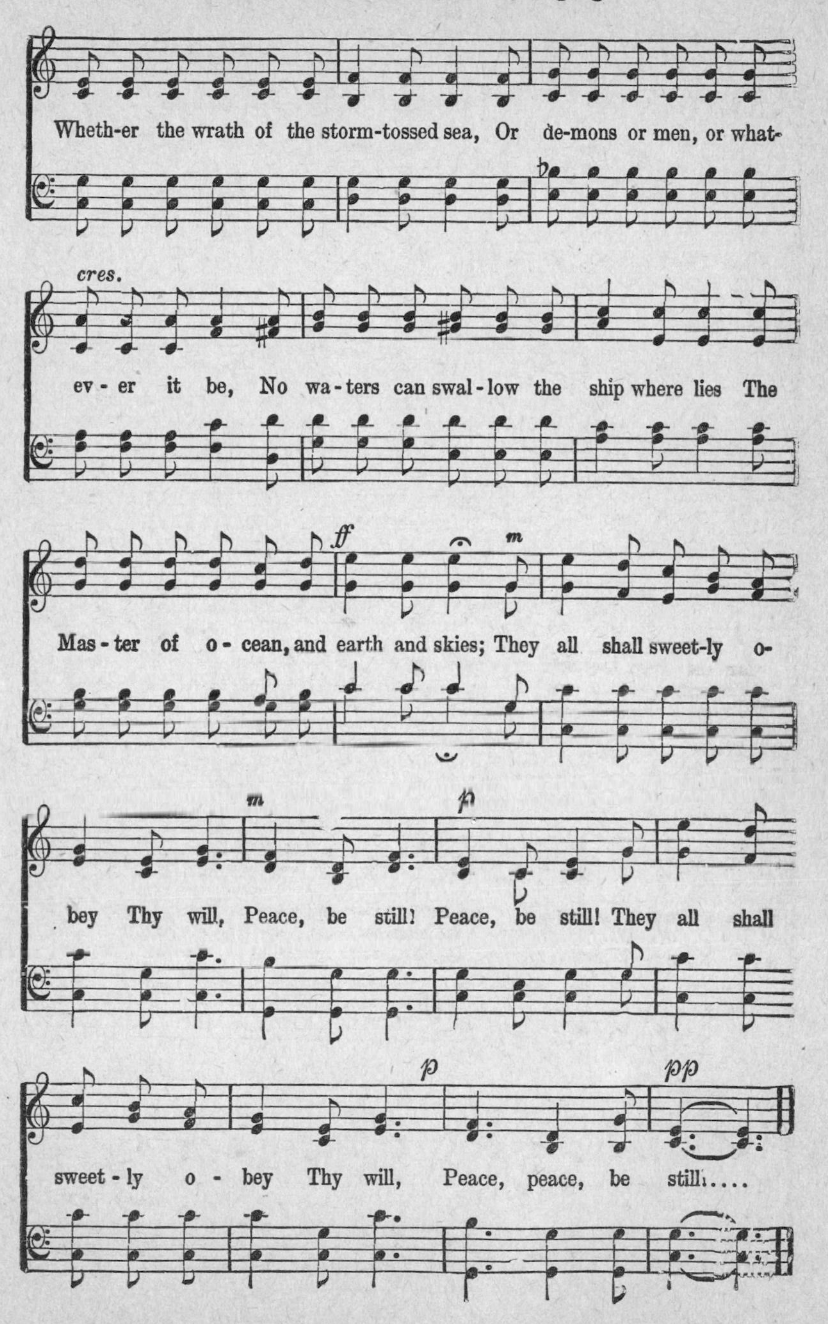
Wheth-er the wrath of the storm-tossed sea, Or de-mons or men, or what-
cres.
ev - er it be, No wa - ters can swal - low the ship where lies The
Mas - ter of o - cean, and earth and skies; They all shall sweet-ly o-
ff
m
bey Thy will, Peace, be still! Peace, be still! They all shall
m
p
sweet - ly o - bey Thy will, Peace, peace, be still....
p
pp

105. Sail On!

COPYRIGHT, 1909, BY CHAS. H. GABRIEL.
NEW ARRANGEMENT COPYRIGHT, 1918, BY HOMER A. RODEHEAVER.
INTERNATIONAL COPYRIGHT SECURED.
C. H. G.
Chas. H. Gabriel.
Solo and Chorus. M. 80
1. Up - on a wide and storm-y sea, Thou'rt sail-ing to e - ter - ni - ty,
2. Art far from shore, and weary-worn—The sky o'er-cast, thy can-vass torn?
3. Do com-rades trem-ble and re-fuse To fur-ther dare the taunt-ing hues?
4. Do snarl-ing waves thy craft as-sail? Art pow'r-less, drift-ing with the gale?
ad lib.
And thy great Ad-m'ral or - ders thee:—"Sail on! sail on! sail on!"
Hark ye! A voice to thee is borne:—"Sail on! sail on! sail on!"
No oth - er course is thine to choose, Sail on! sail on! sail on!
Take heart! God's word shall nev-er fail! Sail on! sail on! sail on!
CHORUS. M. 88
Sail on! sail on! the storms will soon be past, The dark - ness will not al - ways last; Sail on! sail on! God lives! and He commands: "Sail on! sail on!"
sail on! sail on!
on! sail on! sail on! sail on!
rit. e dim.
pp
* May close here

Male Voices

106. The Church in the Wildwood.

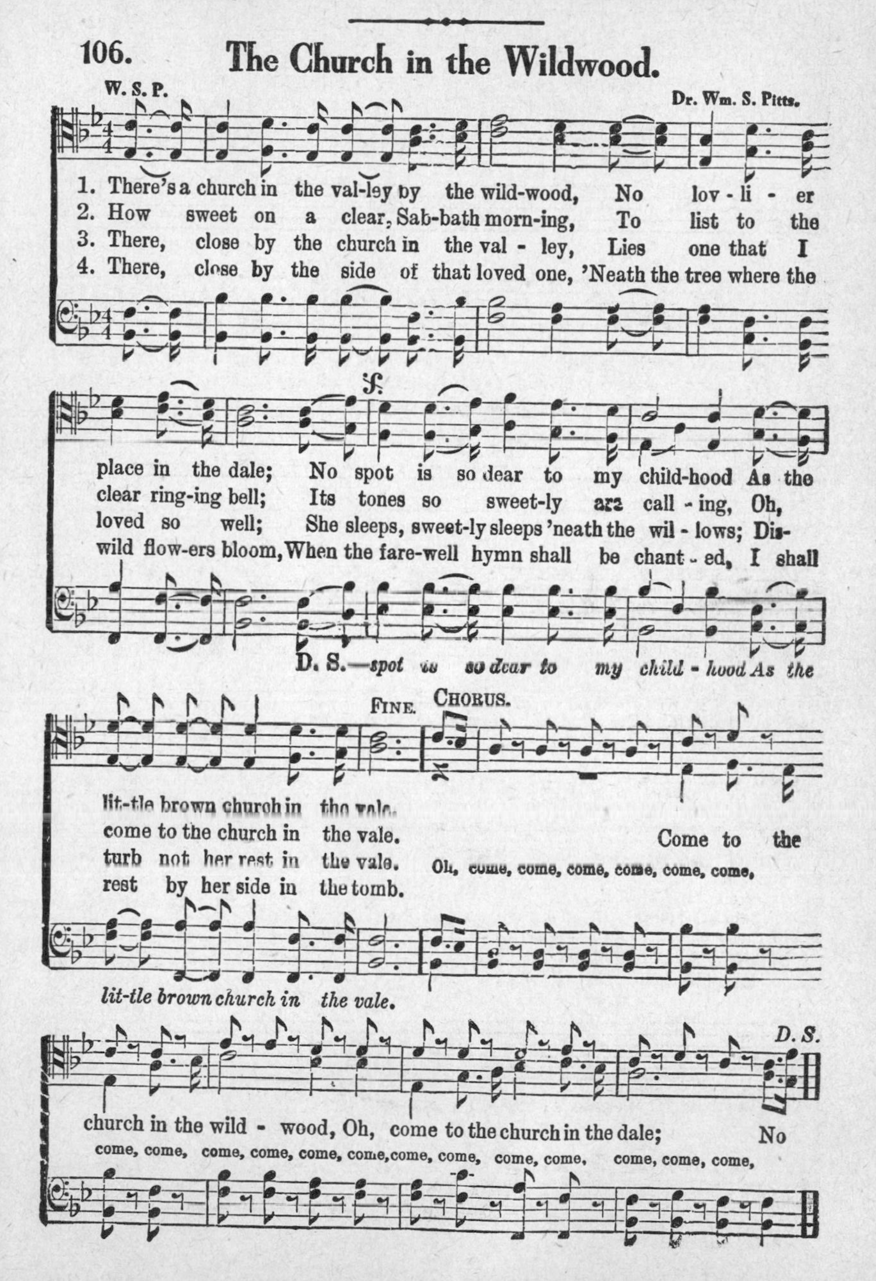
106.
The Church in the Wildwood.
W. S. P.
Dr. Wm. S. Pitts.
1. There's a church in the val-ley by the wild-wood, No lov-li-er
2. How sweet on a clear, Sab-bath morn-ing, To list to the
3. There, close by the church in the val-ley, Lies one that I
4. There, close by the side of that loved one, 'Neath the tree where the
place in the dale; No spot is so dear to my child-hood As the
clear ring-ing bell; Its tones so sweet-ly are call-ing, Oh,
loved so well; She sleeps, sweet-ly sleeps 'neath the wil-lows; Dis-
wild flow-ers bloom, When the fare-well hymn shall be chant-ed, I shall
D. S.—spot is so dear to my child-hood As the
FINE.
CHORUS.
lit-tle brown church in the vale.
come to the church in the vale.
turb not her rest in the vale.
rest by her side in the tomb.
Come to the
Oh, come, come, come, come, come, come,
lit-tle brown church in the vale.
D. S.
church in the wild-wood, Oh, come to the church in the dale;
No
come, come, come, come, come, come, come, come, come, come, come, come, come,

My Anchor Holds.

COPYRIGHT, 1902, BY D. B. TOWNER. CHAS. M. ALEXANDER, OWNER
ARR. COPYRIGHT, 1912, BY CHAS. M. ALEXANDER.
INTERNATIONAL COPYRIGHT SECURED.
W. C. Martin.
D. B. Towner
M. 96 = ♩
1. Tho' the an - gry sur - ges roll On my tem - pest driv - en soul,
2. Might - y tides a - bout me sweep, Per - ils lurk with - in the deep;
3. Troub - les al - most whelm the soul, Griefs like bil - lows o'er me roll;
I am peace - ful, for I know, Wild - ly tho' the winds may blow,
An - gry clouds o'er - shade the sky, And the tem - pest ris - es high;
Tempters seek to lure a - stray, Storms obscure the light of day,
I've an an - chor safe and sure, And in Christ I shall en - dure.
Still I stand the tempest's shock, For my an - chor grips the rock.
But in Christ I can be bold,—I've an an - chor that shall hold.
CHORUS.
And it holds, my an - chor holds; Blow your wild - est, then, ye
And it holds....... my an - chor holds; Blow your wild - - est,
gale, On my bark so small and frail; I shall nev - er, nev - er
then, ye gale,

My Anchor Holds.
fail For my an - chor holds, my an - chor holds.
For my an - chor holds, it firm - ly holds,
108. Just Outside the Door.
COPYRIGHT, 1912, BY B. D. ACKLEY.
HOMER A. RODEHEAVER, OWNER.
James Rowe.
B. D. Ackley.
1. Oh, wea - ry soul, the gate is near, In sin why still a - bide?
2. For - give - ness Je - sus will im-part—To save your soul He died;
3. The day of life is pass - ing by, Soon night your soul will hide;
4. Come in, be free from chains of sin, Be glad, be sat - is - fied;
Both peace and rest are wait - ing here And you are just out-side.
How can you still of - fend His heart, By stay - ing just out-side?
And then "too late" will be your cry, If you are just out-side!
Be - fore the tem-pest breaks, come in, And leave your past out-side.
CHORUS.
Just out-side the door, just out-side the door, Be - hold it stands a - jar!
Just out-side the door, just out-side the door, So near and yet so far!

109 Wandering Child, O Come Home.

COPYRIGHT, 1914, BY HOMER A. RODEHEAVER.
INTERNATIONAL COPYRIGHT SECURED.
Kem G. Bottorf.
Kem G. Bottorf.
Moderato.
1. Have you wandered a-way from your Father's care, Heav-y heart-ed and sad do you roam? There's a sweet, gen-tle voice call-ing now to you—
2. Is your frail bark a-drift on life's rag - ing sea, Are you tossed on its bil-lows and foam? There's a safe har-bor home, wait-ing now for you—
3. He is plead-ing to-day, heed His gen - tle voice, As He bids you no long-er to roam, To that dear Father's house haste with-out de - lay—
Wand'ring child, wand'ring child, O come home.
CHORUS. pp Second time.
Child, come home,
Child, come home, child, come home,
Child, come home,
child, come home,
Wand'ring child, why long - er roam?
Wand'ring child, why long - er roam? 'Tis thy
Wand'ring child, O. come home, come home.
'Tis thy Fa-ther now en-treats— Wand'ring child, come home, come home.
Fa - ther en-treats— Wand'ring child, O come home.

Spirituals.

110. Standin' in the Need of Prayer.

1. Not my brother, nor my sis-ter, but it's me, O Lord, Standin' in the need of prayer;
2. Not the preacher, nor the deacon, but it's me, O Lord, Standin' in the need of prayer;
3. Not my father, nor my moth-er, but it's me, O Lord, Standin' in the need of prayer;
4. Not the stranger, nor my neighbor, but it's me, O Lord, Standin' in the need of prayer;
Not my broth-er, nor my sis-ter, but it's me, O Lord, Standin' in the need of prayer.
Not the preacher, nor the deacon, but it's me, O Lord, Standin' in the need of prayer.
Not my fa-ther, nor my brother, but it's me, O Lord, Standin' in the need of prayer.
Not the stranger, nor my neighbor, but it's me, O Lord, Standin' in the need of prayer.
CHORUS.
It's me, it's me, O Lord, Stand-in' in the need of prayer;
It's me,
standin' in the need of
It's me, it's me, O Lord, Stand-in' in the need of prayer.
prayer;........ It's me,

111. Down By the River-Side.

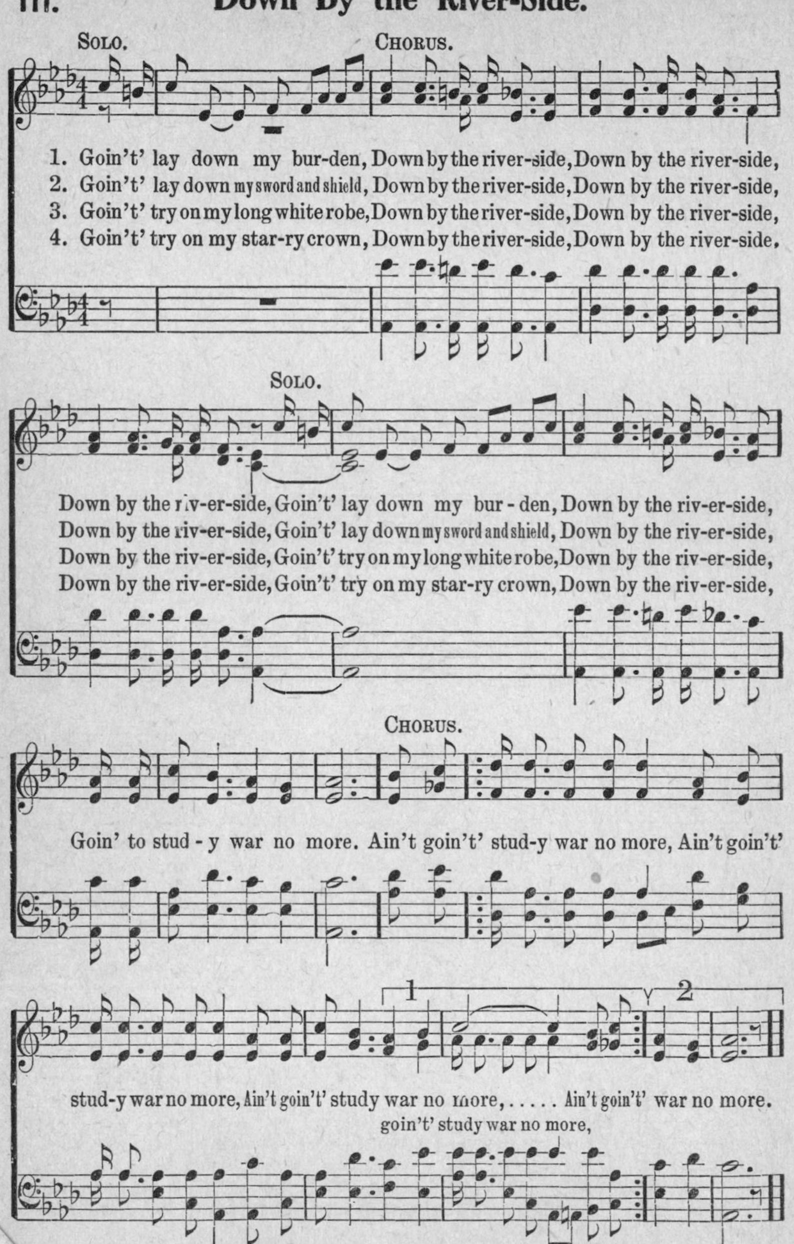
Solo.
Chorus.
1. Goin't' lay down my bur-den, Down by the river-side, Down by the river-side,
2. Goin't' lay down my sword and shield, Down by the river-side, Down by the river-side,
3. Goin't' try on my long white robe, Down by the river-side, Down by the river-side,
4. Goin't' try on my star-ry crown, Down by the river-side, Down by the river-side.
Solo.
Down by the riv-er-side, Goin't' lay down my bur - den, Down by the riv-er-side,
Down by the riv-er-side, Goin't' lay down my sword and shield, Down by the riv-er-side,
Down by the riv-er-side, Goin't' try on my long white robe, Down by the riv-er-side,
Down by the riv-er-side, Goin't' try on my star-ry crown, Down by the riv-er-side,
Chorus.
Goin' to stud - y war no more. Ain't goin't' stud-y war no more, Ain't goin't'
1
2
stud-y war no more, Ain't goin't' study war no more, ... Ain't goin't' war no more.
goin't' study war no more,

5. Goin't' meet my dear old mother.

Goin't' meet my dear old father.

7. Goin't' meet dem Hebrew children.

8. Goin't' meet my loving Jesus.

112. Were You There?
1. Were you there when they cru - ci - fied my Lord? (were you there?)
2. Were you there when they nailed Him to the tree? (to the tree?)
3. Were you there when they pierced Him in the side? (in the side?)
4. Were you there when the sun re - fused to shine? (were you there?)
5. Were you there when they laid Him in the tomb? (in the tomb?)
Were you there when they cru - ci - fied my Lord? Oh!........
Were you there when they nailed Him to the tree? Oh!........
Were you there when they pierced Him in the side? Oh!........
Were you there when the sun re - fused to shine? Oh!........
Were you there when they laid Him in the tomb? Oh!........
Some - times it caus - es me to trem - ble, trem - ble,
Some - times it caus - es me to trem - ble, trem - ble,
Some - times it caus - es me to trem - ble, trem - ble,
Some - times it caus - es me to trem - ble, trem - ble,
Some - times it caus - es me to trem - ble, trem - ble,
trem - ble, Were you there when they cru - ci - fied my Lord?
trem - ble, Were you there when they nailed Him to the tree?
trem - ble, Were you there when they pierced Him in the side?
trem - ble, Were you there when the sun re - fused to shine?
trem - ble, Were you there when they laid Him in the tomb?

113 Hush! Somebody's Calling My Name.

(MIXED VOICES.)

Arr. by J. B. Herbert.

p CHORUS.
mp
Hush! hush! somebody's call-ing my name; Hush! hush! somebody's calling my
p
name; Hush! hush! some-bod-y's call - ing my name; O my Lord, O my
rit.
FINE.
Animated.
Lord, what shall I do?
1. I'm so glad that troub-le don't last al-
2. I'm so glad I got my re - lig-ion in
3. I'm so glad my soul's got a hid - ing-
1
ways; I'm so glad that troub-le don't last al-
time; I'm so glad I got my re - lig-ion in
place; I'm so glad my soul's got a hid - ing
Hal - le - lu - jah!
2
rit.
D. C.
ways; ways; O my Lord, O my Lord, what shall I do?
time; time; O my Lord, O my Lord, what shall I do?
place; place; O my Lord, O my Lord, what shall I do?
O glo - ry!

Devotional Songs.

114. Savior, More Than Life.

Fanny J. Crosby. Copyright, 1908, by W. H. Doane. W. H. Doane.

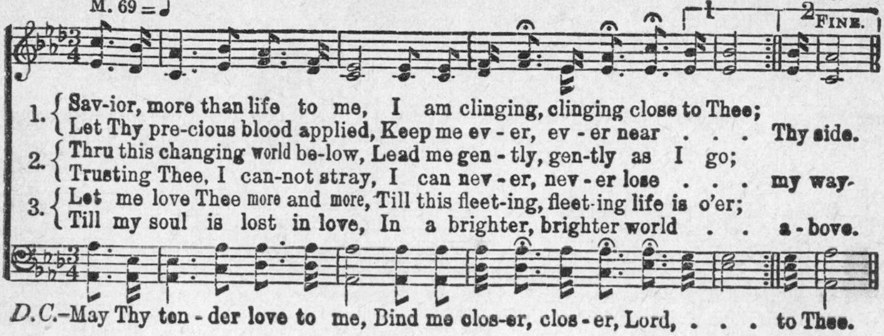

M. 69 = ♩

1. { Sav-ior, more than life to me, I am clinging, clinging close to Thee;
Let Thy pre-cious blood applied, Keep me ev - er, ev - er near . . . Thy side.

2. { Thru this changing world be-low, Lead me gen - tly, gen-tly as I go;
Trusting Thee, I can-not stray, I can nev - er, nev - er lose . . . my way.

3. { Let me love Thee more and more, Till this fleet-ing, fleet-ing life is o'er;
Till my soul is lost in love, In a brighter, brighter world . . . a - bove.

D.C.–May Thy ten - der love to me, Bind me clos-er, clos-er, Lord, . . . to Thee.

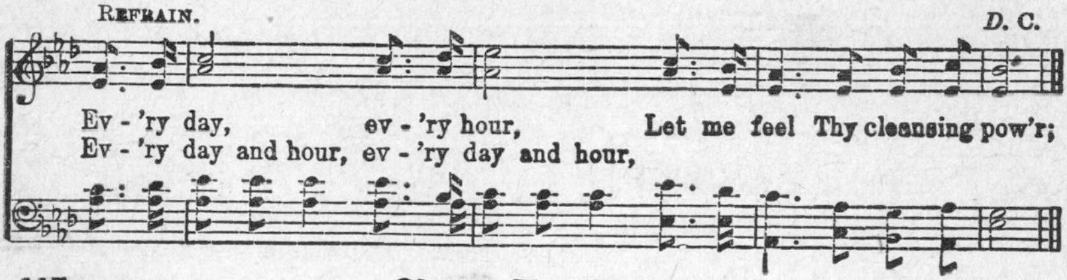

REFRAIN. D. C.

Ev - 'ry day, ev - 'ry hour, Let me feel Thy cleansing pow'r;
Ev - 'ry day and hour, ev - 'ry day and hour,

115. Close To Thee.

Fanny J. Crosby. S. J. Vail.

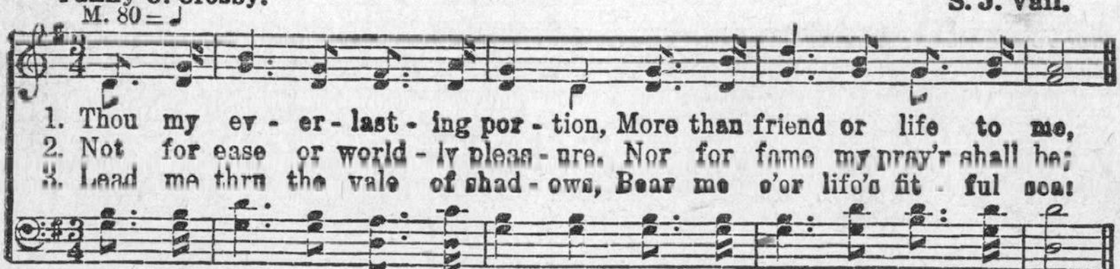

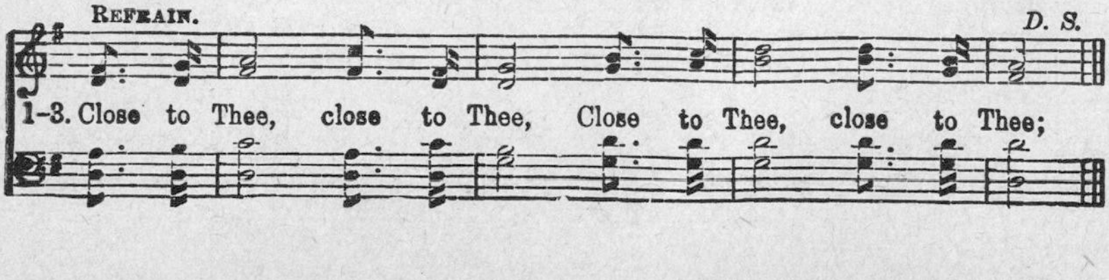

M. 80 = ♩

1. Thou my ev - er - last - ing por - tion, More than friend or life to me,
2. Not for ease or world - ly pleas - ure, Nor for fame my pray'r shall be;
3. Lead me thru the vale of shad - ows, Bear me o'er life's fit - ful sea;

All a - long my pil - grim jour - ney, Sav - ior, let me walk with Thee.
Glad - ly will I toil and suf - fer, On - ly let me walk with Thee.
Then the gate of life e - ter - nal, May I en - ter, Lord, with Thee.

D.S.–All a - long my pil - grim jour - ney, Sav - ior, let me walk with Thee.
Glad - ly will I toil and suf - fer, On - ly let me walk with Thee.
Then the gate of life e - ter - nal, May I en - ter, Lord, with Thee.

REFRAIN. D. S.

1-3. Close to Thee, close to Thee, Close to Thee, close to Thee;

116.

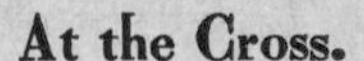
At the Cross.

COPYRIGHT. 1885, BY R. E. HUDSON.
USED BY PER.
Isaac Watts.
R. E. Hudson.
1. { Alas! and did my Savior bleed, And did my Sov'reign die,
Would He devote that sa- cred head For such a worm as I?
2. { Was it for crimes that I have done, He groan'd upon the tree,
A - maz-ing pit-y, grace unknown! And love beyond degree
CHORUS.
At the cross, at the cross, where I first saw the light, And the burden of my heart roll'd a-
way, It was there by faith I received my sight, And now I am happy all the day.
roll'd a-way,
117.
Hold the Fort.
THE JOHN CHURCH CO. OWNERS.
USED BY PERMISSION.
P. P. B.
P. P. Bliss.
1. { Ho, my comrades! see the signal Wav-ing in the sky!
Re-in-force-ments now appearing, Vic - to - ry is nigh.
2. { See the mighty host ad-vanc-ing, Sa - tan lead-ing on:
Mighty men a-round us fall-ing, Cour-age al-most gone!
3. { See the glorious banner waving! Hear the trumpet blow!
In our Leader's name we'll triumph O - ver ev-'ry foe.
4. { Fierce and long the bat-tle rag-es, But our help is near;
Onward comes our great Commander, Cheer, my comrades, cheer.
CHORUS.
"Hold the fort, for I am coming," Jesus signals still; Wave the answer back to heaven, "By Thy grace we will."

118 All Hail the Power of Jesus' Name.
E. Perronet.
First Tune
James Ellor.
1. All hail the pow'r of Jesus' name! Let angels prostrate fall, Let angels prostrate fall; Bring forth the royal diadem,
And crown.......................... Him, Crown Him, crown Him, crown Him;
And crown Him, crown Him, crown Him, crown Him, And crown Him Lord of all, crown Him, And crown Him Lord of all!
And crown.......................... Him, Crown Him, crown... Him;
And crown Him, crown Him, crown Him, Crown.......................... Him; And crown Him Lord of all.
2 Ye chosen seed of Israel's race,
Ye ransomed from the fall;
Hail Him who saves you by His grace,
And crown Him Lord of all.
3 Let every kindred, every tribe,
On this terrestrial ball,
To Him all majesty ascribe,
And crown Him Lord of all.
4 O that with yonder sacred throng
We at His feet may fall,
We'll join the everlasting song,
And crown Him Lord of all.
119. All Hail the Power of Jesus' Name.
Edward Perronet.
Second Tune.
William Schrubsole.
1. All hail the pow'r of Je-sus' name, Let an-gels pros-trate fall; Bring forth the roy-al di - a - dem,
And crown Him Lord of all; Bring forth the roy - al di - a - dem, And crown Him Lord of all.
120. Work, For the Night is Coming.
Annie L. Walker.
FINE.
L. Mason.
1. Work for the night is com-ing, Work thro' the morning hours;
Work while the dew is sparkling, Work 'mid springing flow'rs. Work when the day grows
D.C.—Work for the night is coming, When man's work is done.
brighter, Work in the glowing sun,
D. C.
2 Work, for the night is coming,
Work through the sunny noon;
Fill brightest hours with labor,
Rest comes sure and soon.
Give every flying minute,
Something to keep in store;
Work, for the night is coming,
When man works no more.
3 Work, for the night is coming,
Under the sunset sky;
While the bright tints are glowing,
Work, for daylight flies.
Work till the last beam fadeth,
Fadeth to shine no more,
Work while the night is darkening,
When man's work is o'er.

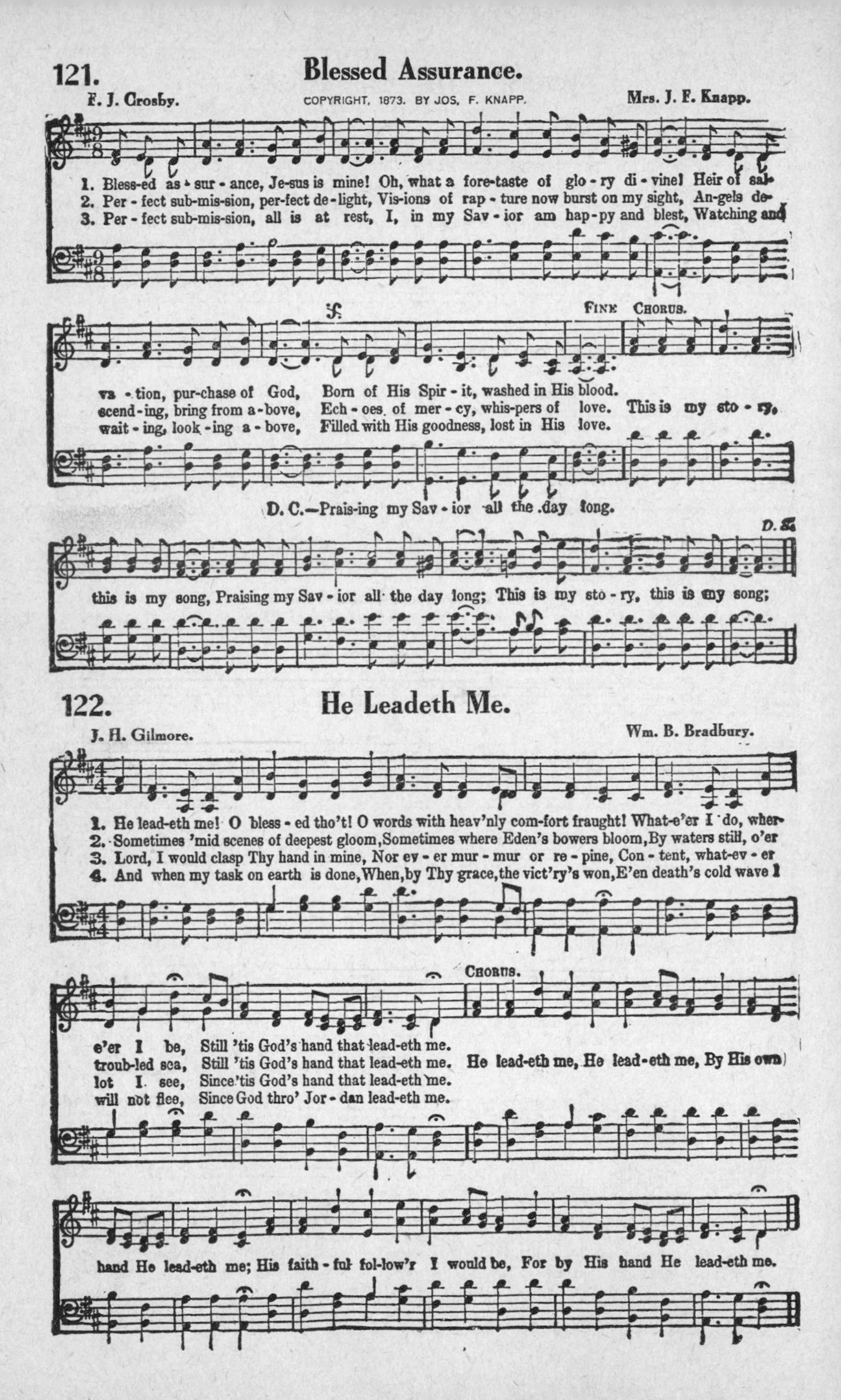
121.
Blessed Assurance.
F. J. Crosby.
COPYRIGHT, 1873, BY JOS. F. KNAPP.
Mrs. J. F. Knapp.
1. Bless-ed as - sur - ance, Je-sus is mine! Oh, what a fore-taste of glo - ry di - vine! Heir of sal-
2. Per - fect sub-mis-sion, per-fect de-light, Vis-ions of rap - ture now burst on my sight, An-gels de-
3. Per - fect sub-mis-sion, all is at rest, I, in my Sav - ior am hap-py and blest, Watching and
FINE
CHORUS.
va - tion, pur-chase of God, Born of His Spir - it, washed in His blood.
scend-ing, bring from a-bove, Ech - oes of mer - cy, whis-pers of love. This is my sto - ry,
wait - ing, look - ing a - bove, Filled with His goodness, lost in His love.
D. C.—Prais-ing my Sav - ior all the day long.
D. S.
this is my song, Praising my Sav - ior all the day long; This is my sto - ry, this is my song;
122.
He Leadeth Me.
J. H. Gilmore.
Wm. B. Bradbury.
1. He lead-eth me! O bless - ed tho't! O words with heav'nly com-fort fraught! What-e'er I do, wher-
2. Sometimes 'mid scenes of deepest gloom, Sometimes where Eden's bowers bloom, By waters still, o'er
3. Lord, I would clasp Thy hand in mine, Nor ev - er mur - mur or re - pine, Con - tent, what-ev - er
4. And when my task on earth is done, When, by Thy grace, the vict'ry's won, E'en death's cold wave I
CHORUS.
e'er I be, Still 'tis God's hand that lead-eth me.
troub-led sea, Still 'tis God's hand that lead-eth me. He lead-eth me, He lead-eth me, By His own
lot I see, Since 'tis God's hand that lead-eth me.
will not flee, Since God thro' Jor - dan lead-eth me.
hand He lead-eth me; His faith - ful fol-low'r I would be, For by His hand He lead-eth me.

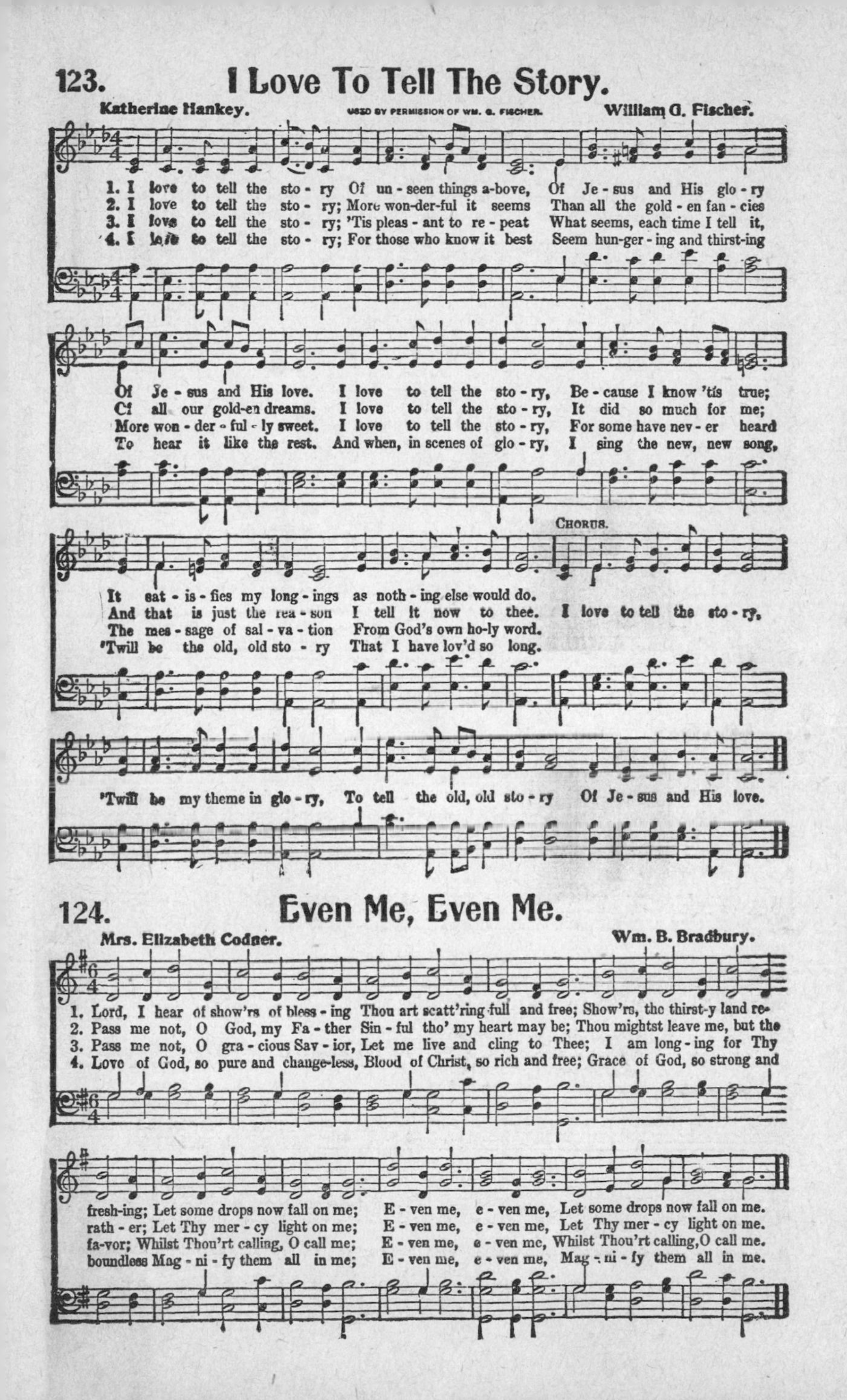
123. I Love To Tell The Story.
Katherine Hankey.
USED BY PERMISSION OF WM. G. FISCHER.
William G. Fischer.
1. I love to tell the sto - ry Of un - seen things a-bove, Of Je - sus and His glo - ry
2. I love to tell the sto - ry; More won-der-ful it seems Than all the gold - en fan - cies
3. I love to tell the sto - ry; 'Tis pleas - ant to re - peat What seems, each time I tell it,
4. I love to tell the sto - ry; For those who know it best Seem hun-ger - ing and thirst-ing
Of Je - sus and His love. I love to tell the sto - ry, Be - cause I know 'tis true;
Of all our gold-en dreams. I love to tell the sto - ry, It did so much for me;
More won - der - ful - ly sweet. I love to tell the sto - ry, For some have nev - er heard
To hear it like the rest. And when, in scenes of glo - ry, I sing the new, new song,
CHORUS.
It sat - is - fies my long - ings as noth - ing else would do.
And that is just the rea - son I tell it now to thee.
The mes - sage of sal - va - tion From God's own ho - ly word.
'Twill be the old, old sto - ry That I have lov'd so long.
I love to tell the sto - ry,
'Twill be my theme in glo - ry, To tell the old, old sto - ry Of Je - sus and His love.
124. Even Me, Even Me.
Mrs. Elizabeth Codner.
Wm. B. Bradbury.
1. Lord, I hear of show'rs of bless - ing Thou art scatt'ring full and free; Show'rs, the thirst-y land re-
2. Pass me not, O God, my Fa - ther Sin - ful tho' my heart may be; Thou mightst leave me, but the
3. Pass me not, O gra - cious Sav - ior, Let me live and cling to Thee; I am long - ing for Thy
4. Love of God, so pure and change-less, Blood of Christ, so rich and free; Grace of God, so strong and
fresh-ing; Let some drops now fall on me; E - ven me, e - ven me, Let some drops now fall on me.
rath - er; Let Thy mer - cy light on me; E - ven me, e - ven me, Let Thy mer - cy light on me.
fa-vor; Whilst Thou'rt calling, O call me; E - ven me, e - ven me, Whilst Thou'rt calling, O call me.
boundless Mag - ni - fy them all in me; E - ven me, e - ven me, Mag - ni - fy them all in me.

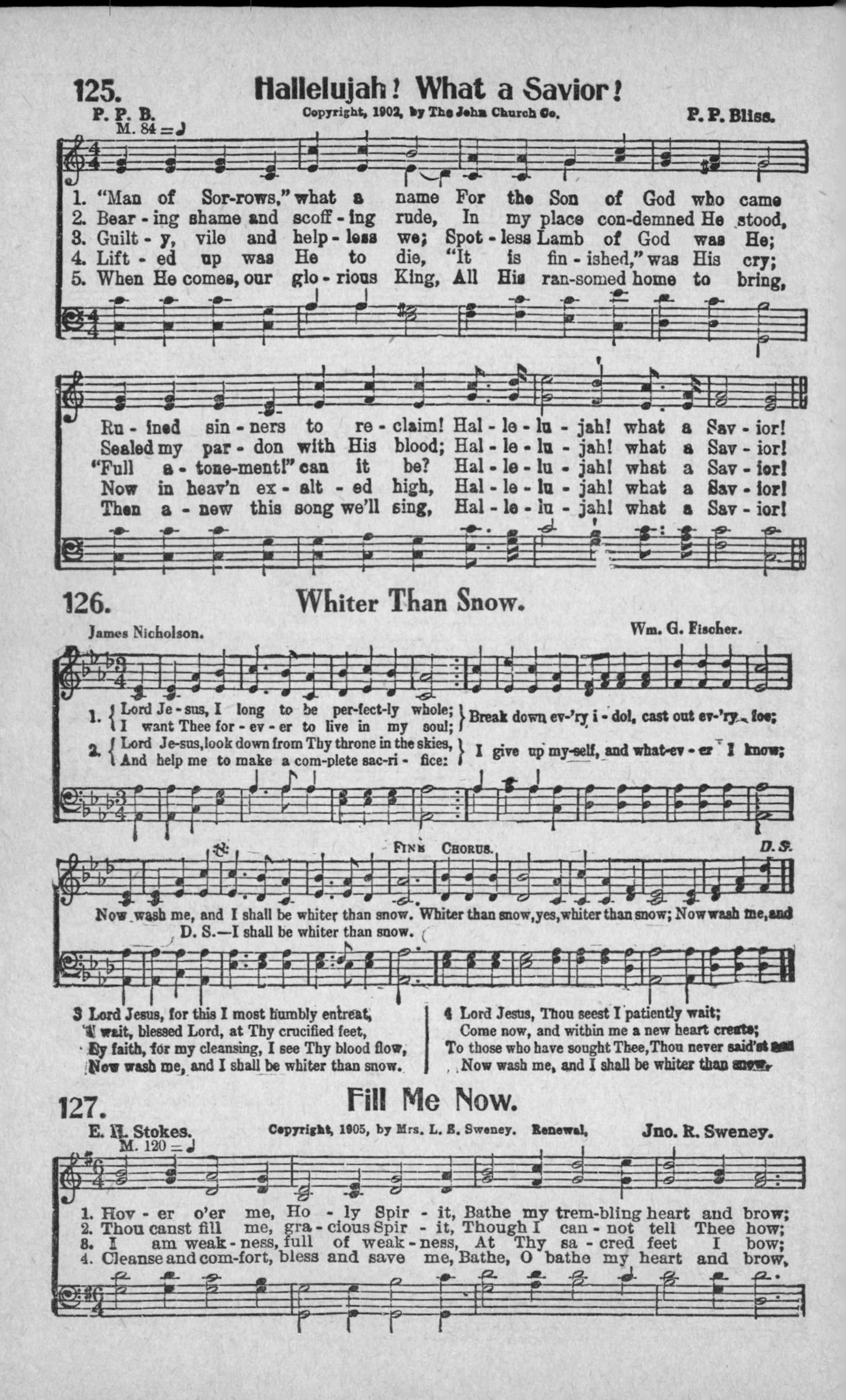
125.
Hallelujah! What a Savior!
P. P. B.
Copyright, 1902, by The John Church Co.
P. P. Bliss.
M. 84 = ♩
1. "Man of Sor-rows," what a name For the Son of God who came
2. Bear - ing shame and scoff - ing rude, In my place con-demned He stood,
3. Guilt - y, vile and help - less we; Spot - less Lamb of God was He;
4. Lift - ed up was He to die, "It is fin - ished," was His cry;
5. When He comes, our glo - rious King, All His ran-somed home to bring,
Ru - ined sin - ners to re - claim! Hal - le - lu - jah! what a Sav - ior!
Sealed my par - don with His blood; Hal - le - lu - jah! what a Sav - ior!
"Full a - tone-ment!" can it be? Hal - le - lu - jah! what a Sav - ior!
Now in heav'n ex - alt - ed high, Hal - le - lu - jah! what a Sav - ior!
Then a - new this song we'll sing, Hal - le - lu - jah! what a Sav - ior!
126.
Whiter Than Snow.
James Nicholson.
Wm. G. Fischer.
1. Lord Je - sus, I long to be per-fect-ly whole; I want Thee for - ev - er to live in my soul; Break down ev-'ry i - dol, cast out ev-'ry foe;
2. Lord Je-sus, look down from Thy throne in the skies, And help me to make a com-plete sac-ri - fice: I give up my-self, and what-ev - er I know;
Fine Chorus. D. S.
Now wash me, and I shall be whiter than snow. Whiter than snow, yes, whiter than snow; Now wash me, and
D. S.—I shall be whiter than snow.
3 Lord Jesus, for this I most humbly entreat,
I wait, blessed Lord, at Thy crucified feet,
By faith, for my cleansing, I see Thy blood flow,
Now wash me, and I shall be whiter than snow.
4 Lord Jesus, Thou seest I patiently wait;
Come now, and within me a new heart create;
To those who have sought Thee, Thou never said'st no,
Now wash me, and I shall be whiter than snow.
127.
Fill Me Now.
E. H. Stokes.
Copyright, 1905, by Mrs. L. E. Sweney. Renewal.
Jno. R. Sweney.
M. 120 = ♩
1. Hov - er o'er me, Ho - ly Spir - it, Bathe my trem-bling heart and brow;
2. Thou canst fill me, gra - cious Spir - it, Though I can - not tell Thee how;
3. I am weak - ness, full of weak - ness, At Thy sa - cred feet I bow;
4. Cleanse and com-fort, bless and save me, Bathe, O bathe my heart and brow,

Fill Me Now.

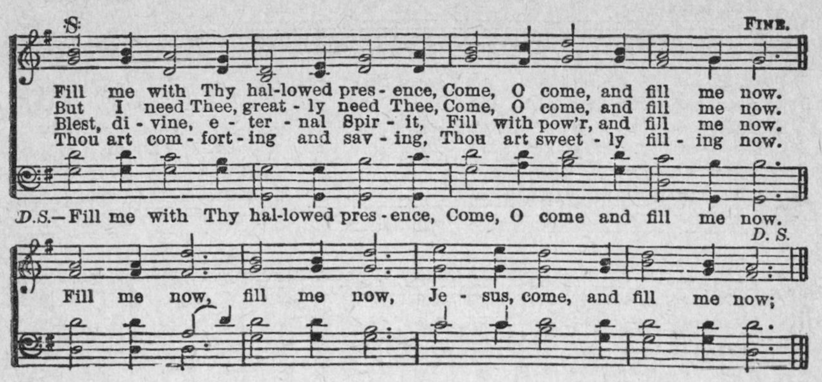

FINE.
Fill me with Thy hal-lowed pres-ence, Come, O come, and fill me now.
But I need Thee, great-ly need Thee, Come, O come, and fill me now.
Blest, di-vine, e-ter-nal Spir-it, Fill with pow'r, and fill me now.
Thou art com-fort-ing and sav-ing, Thou art sweet-ly fill-ing now.
D.S.—Fill me with Thy hal-lowed pres-ence, Come, O come and fill me now.
D. S.
Fill me now, fill me now, Je-sus, come, and fill me now;

D.S.
1. Nearer my God to Thee, Nearer to Thee,
E'en tho' it be a cross, (Omit.) That raiseth me, Still all my song shall be, Nearer, my God, to Thee,
D.S.—Nearer, my God, to Thee, (Omit.) Near-er to Thee.
1. There's a wide-ness in God's mer-cy, Like the wide-ness of the sea, There's a kind-ness in His justice, Which is more than lib-er-ty.
2. There is wel-come for the sin-ner, And more grac-es for the good; There is mer-cy with the Savior, There is heal-ing in His blood.

128. Nearer, My God, to Thee.

Mrs. Sarah F. Adams. Lowell Mason.

2 Though like a wanderer,
The sun gone down,
Darkness be over me,
My rest a stone;
Yet in my dreams I'd be
Nearer, my God, to Thee;
Nearer to Thee!

3 There let the way appear
Steps unto heaven;
All that Thou sendest me,
In mercy given;
Angels to beckon me
Nearer, my God, to Thee;
Nearer to Thee!

4 Or if, on joyful wing,
Cleaving the sky,
Sun, moon, and stars forgot,
Upward I fly,
Still all my song shall be,
Nearer, my God, to Thee,
Nearer to Thee!

129. There's a Wideness.

Frederick W. Faber. Lizzie S. Tourjee.

3 For the love of God is broader
Than the measure of man's mind;
And the heart of the Eternal,
Is most wonderfully kind.

4 If our love were but more simple,
We should take Him at His word;
And our lives would be all sunshine
In the sweetness of our Lord.

130. Loving Kindness.
Samuel Medley.
Anon.
1. A-wake my soul in joy-ful lays And sing my great Redeemer's praise, He justly claims a song from me,
2. He saw me ru - ined in the fall, Yet loved me not-with-stand-ing all; He saved me from my lost estate,
3. Tho' numerous hosts of mighty foes, Tho' earth and hell my way op-pose, He safely leads my soul a-long,
4. When trouble, like a gloomy cloud, Has gathered thick and thundered loud, He near my soul has always stood,
His lov - ing kindness, oh, how free! Loving kindness, loving kind-ness, His loving kindness, oh, how free!
His lov - ing kindness, oh, how great! Loving kindness, loving kind-ness, His loving kindness, oh, how great!
His lov - ing kindness, oh, how strong! Loving kindness, loving kind-ness, His loving kindness, oh, how strong!
His lov - ing kindness, oh, how good! Loving kindness, loving kind-ness, His loving kindness, oh, how good!
131. Holy, Holy, Holy.
Reginald Heber.
John B. Dykes.
1. Ho-ly, ho-ly, ho - ly, Lord God Al-might-y! Ear - ly in the morn-ing our song shall rise to Thee;
2. Ho-ly, ho-ly, ho - ly, all the saints adore Thee, Casting down their golden crowns around the glassy sea;
3. Ho-ly, ho-ly, ho - ly, tho' the darkness hide Thee, Tho' the eye of sin-ful man Thy glory may not see;
4. Ho-ly, ho-ly, ho - ly, Lord God Almighty! All Thy works shall praise Thy name, in earth, and sky, and sea;
Ho - ly, ho - ly, ho - ly, mer - ci - ful and might - y, God in Three Persons, bless-ed Trin - i - ty!
Cher-u-bim and sera - phim fall - ing down be - fore Thee, Which wert and art, and ev-er-more shalt be.
On - ly Thou art ho - ly, there is none be - side Thee, Per-fect in pow-er, in love, and pu - ri - ty.
Ho - ly, ho - ly, ho - ly, mer - ci - ful and might - y, God in Three Persons, bless-ed Trin - i - ty.
132. Ring the Bells of Heaven.
COPYRIGHT, 1903, BY THE JOHN CHURCH CO.
USED BY PERMISSION.
Rev. Wm. O. Cushing.
Geo. F. Root.
Joyfully.
FINE.
1. Ring the bells of heaven! there is joy to-day, For a soul re-turn-ing from the wild;
See! the Father meets him out upon the way, Wel-coming His weary wand'ring child.
2. Ring the bells of heaven! there is joy to-day, For the wand'rer now is re-con-ciled;
Yes, a soul is rescued from his sinful way, And is born a-new a ransomed child.
3. Ring the bells of heaven! spread the feast today, Angels swell the glad triumphant strain,
Tell the joy-ful tidings! bear it far a - way, For a precious soul is born a - gain.
D.C.—'Tis the ransom'd army, like a mighty sea, Pealing forth the anthem of the free.

Ring the Bells of Heaven.

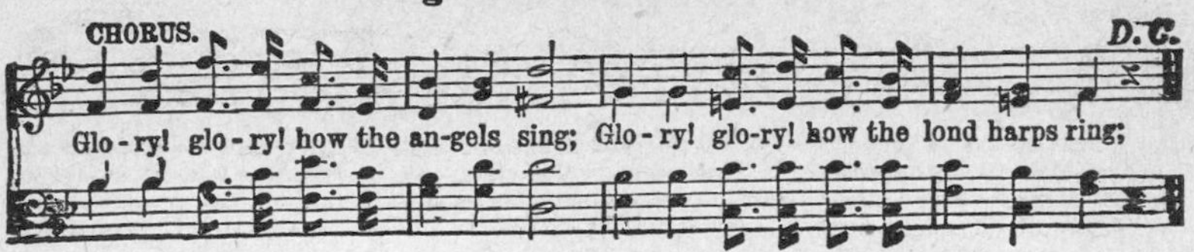
CHORUS.
D.C.
Glo - ry! glo - ry! how the an-gels sing; Glo - ry! glo - ry! how the lond harps ring;

133. The Son of God Goes Forth to War.

R. Heber. H. S. Cutler.

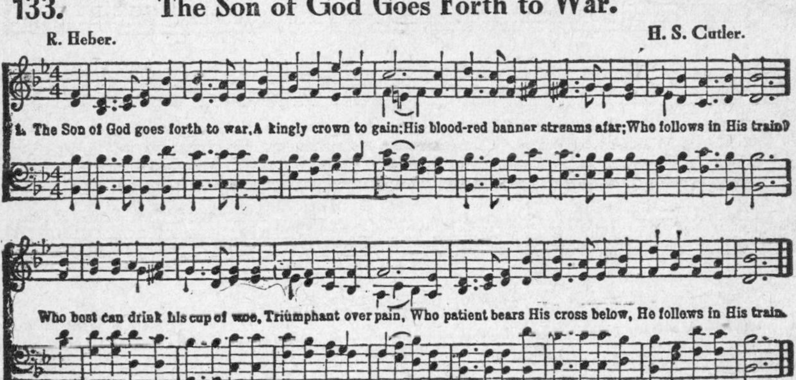
1. The Son of God goes forth to war, A kingly crown to gain; His blood-red banner streams afar; Who follows in His train?
Who best can drink his cup of woe, Triumphant over pain, Who patient bears His cross below, He follows in His train.

2 That martyr first, whose eagle eye
Could pierce beyond the grave;
Who saw His Master in the sky;
And called on Him to save.
Like Him, with pardon on His tongue
In midst of mortal pain,
He pray'd for them that did the wrong,
Who follows in His train?

3 A noble band, the chosen few,
On whom the Spirit came;
Twelve valiant saints, their hope they knew,
And mock'd the cross and flame.
They met the tyrant's brandish'd steel,
The lion's gory mane;
They bowed their heads the stroke to feel,
Who follows in their train?

4 A noble army, men and boys,
The matron and the maid,
Around the Savior's throne rejoice,
In robes of light arrayed;
They climbed the steep ascent of heav'n
Thro' peril, toil, and pain,
O God, to us may grace be giv'n
To follow in their train.

134. Stand Up for Jesus.

George Duffield. G. J. Webb.

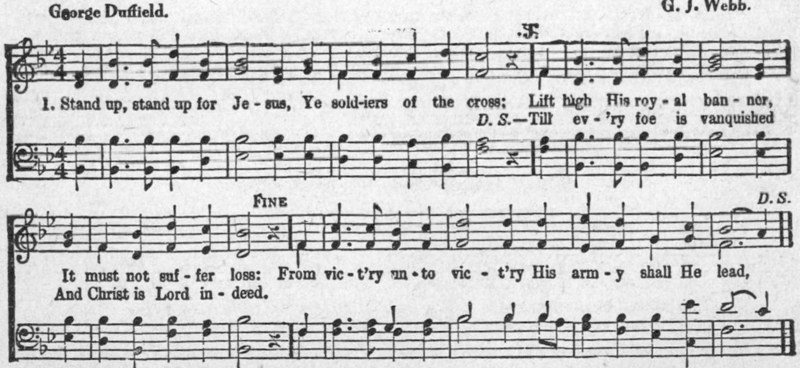
1. Stand up, stand up for Je - sus, Ye sold-iers of the cross; Lift high His roy - al ban - ner,
D. S.—Till ev - 'ry foe is vanquished
FINE
D. S.
It must not suf - fer loss: From vic - t'ry un - to vic - t'ry His arm - y shall He lead,
And Christ is Lord in - deed.

2 Stand up, stand up for Jesus,
The trumpet call obey;
Forth to the mighty conflict,
In this His glorious day,
"Ye that are men, now serve Him,"
Against unnumbered foes;
Your courage rise with danger,
And strength to strength oppose.

3 Stand up, stand up for Jesus,
Stand in His strength alone;
The arm of flesh will fail you;
Ye dare not trust your own,
Put on the gospel armor,
Each piece put on with prayer;
Where duty calls, or danger,
Be never wanting there.

4 Stand up, stand up for Jesus,
The strife will not be long;
This day the noise of battle,
The next the victor's song;
To Him that overcometh,
A crown of life shall be;
He with the King of glory
Shall reign eternally.

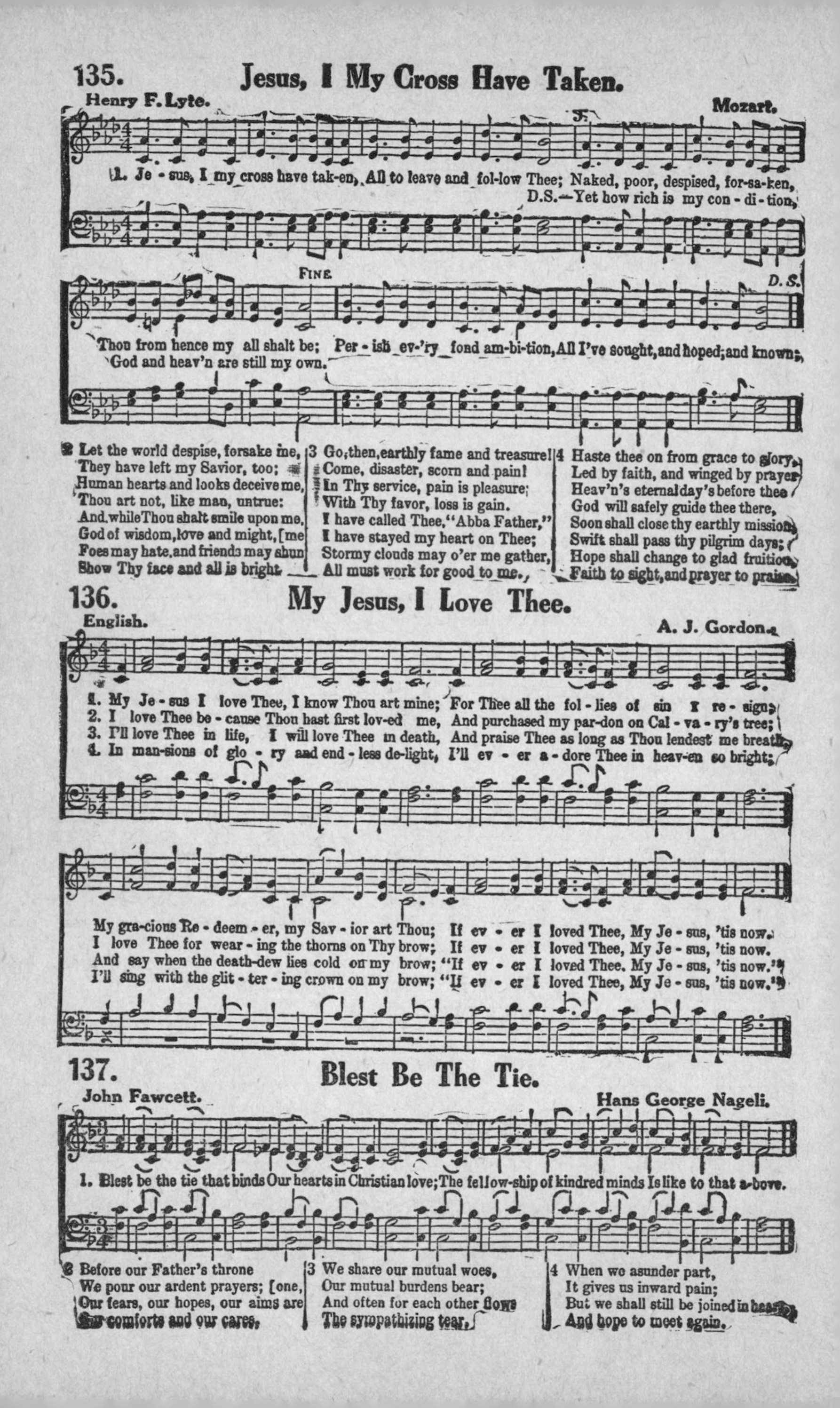
135. Jesus, I My Cross Have Taken.
Henry F. Lyte.
Mozart.
1. Je - sus, I my cross have tak-en, All to leave and fol-low Thee; Naked, poor, despised, for-sa-ken,
D.S.—Yet how rich is my con - di - tion,
FINE
D. S.
Thou from hence my all shalt be; Per - ish ev-'ry fond am-bi-tion, All I've sought, and hoped, and known;
God and heav'n are still my own.
2 Let the world despise, forsake me,
They have left my Savior, too;
Human hearts and looks deceive me,
Thou art not, like man, untrue:
And while Thou shalt smile upon me,
God of wisdom, love and might, [me
Foes may hate, and friends may shun
Show Thy face and all is bright.
3 Go, then, earthly fame and treasure!
Come, disaster, scorn and pain!
In Thy service, pain is pleasure;
With Thy favor, loss is gain.
I have called Thee, "Abba Father,"
I have stayed my heart on Thee;
Stormy clouds may o'er me gather,
All must work for good to me.
4 Haste thee on from grace to glory,
Led by faith, and winged by prayer
Heav'n's eternal day's before thee
God will safely guide thee there,
Soon shall close thy earthly mission
Swift shall pass thy pilgrim days;
Hope shall change to glad fruition
Faith to sight, and prayer to praise.
136. My Jesus, I Love Thee.
English.
A. J. Gordon.
1. My Je - sus I love Thee, I know Thou art mine; For Thee all the fol - lies of sin I re - sign;
2. I love Thee be - cause Thou hast first lov-ed me, And purchased my par-don on Cal - va - ry's tree;
3. I'll love Thee in life, I will love Thee in death, And praise Thee as long as Thou lendest me breath,
4. In man-sions of glo - ry and end - less de-light, I'll ev - er a - dore Thee in heav-en so bright;
My gra-cious Re - deem - er, my Sav - ior art Thou; If ev - er I loved Thee, My Je - sus, 'tis now.
I love Thee for wear - ing the thorns on Thy brow; If ev - er I loved Thee, My Je - sus, 'tis now.
And say when the death-dew lies cold on my brow; "If ev - er I loved Thee, My Je - sus, 'tis now."
I'll sing with the glit - ter - ing crown on my brow; "If ev - er I loved Thee, My Je - sus, 'tis now."
137. Blest Be The Tie.
John Fawcett.
Hans George Nageli.
1. Blest be the tie that binds Our hearts in Christian love; The fel-low-ship of kindred minds Is like to that a-bove.
2 Before our Father's throne
We pour our ardent prayers; [one,
Our fears, our hopes, our aims are
Our comforts and our cares.
3 We share our mutual woes,
Our mutual burdens bear;
And often for each other flows
The sympathizing tear.
4 When we asunder part,
It gives us inward pain;
But we shall still be joined in heart,
And hope to meet again.

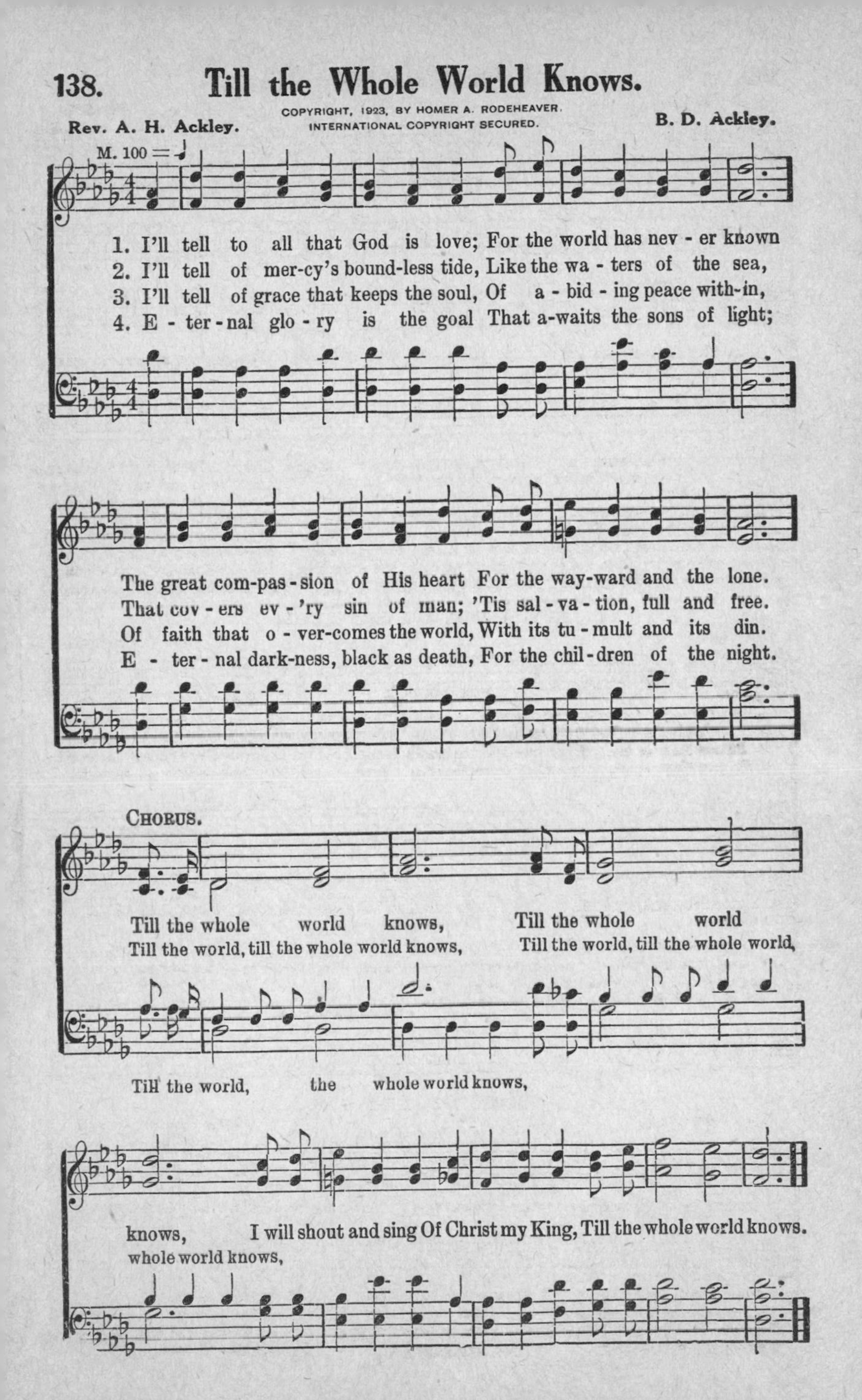
138. Till the Whole World Knows.
COPYRIGHT, 1923, BY HOMER A. RODEHEAVER.
INTERNATIONAL COPYRIGHT SECURED.
Rev. A. H. Ackley.
B. D. Ackley.
M. 100 =
1. I'll tell to all that God is love; For the world has nev - er known
2. I'll tell of mer-cy's bound-less tide, Like the wa - ters of the sea,
3. I'll tell of grace that keeps the soul, Of a - bid - ing peace with-in,
4. E - ter - nal glo - ry is the goal That a-waits the sons of light;
The great com-pas - sion of His heart For the way-ward and the lone.
That cov - ers ev - 'ry sin of man; 'Tis sal - va - tion, full and free.
Of faith that o - ver-comes the world, With its tu - mult and its din.
E - ter - nal dark-ness, black as death, For the chil - dren of the night.
CHORUS.
Till the whole world knows, Till the whole world
Till the world, till the whole world knows, Till the world, till the whole world,
Till the world, the whole world knows,
knows, I will shout and sing Of Christ my King, Till the whole world knows.
whole world knows,

139. Song To the Flag.

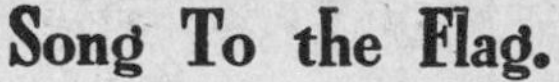

COPYRIGHT, 1910, BY ACKLEY AND RODEHEAVER.
HOMER A. RODEHEAVER, OWNER.

Edith Sanford Tillotson. B. D. Ackley.

M. 100 = ♩
1. Ban - ner bright, with thy col - ors shin - ing o'er us,
2. Crim - son bars, you can speak to us of cour - age;
3. Star - gemmed flag, may thy chil - dren long re - mem - ber
Dear bright flag and the em - blem of the free;
Snow - y white, give us peace - ful hearts and pure;
What great price has been paid thy folds to raise;
Hearts beat high when we see thee wave a - bove us,
Loy - al blue, may our lives in truth be ground - ed,
May we live to be wor - thy of thy keep - ing,
Free - dom's sign art thou o - ver land, o - ver sea:
So we'll wear our col - ors while time shall en - dure:
May we show thee hon - or, de - vo - tion and praise.
CHORUS.
Heart and hand we'll pledge to star - ry ban - ner Staunch and

Song To the Flag.

strong we'll stand to col - ors true! Day by day we'll serve with
best en - deav - or, Life's al - le-giance give to the red, white and blue.
After Chorus last time, or may be used after each verse if desired.
Three cheers for the red, white and blue! Three
cheers for the red, white and blue! The ar - my and na - vy for-
ev - er, Three cheers for the red, white and blue!

140 O HAPPY DAY

O happy day that fixed my choice
On Thee, my Savior and my God!
Well may this glowing heart rejoice,
And tell its raptures all abroad.

Happy day, happy day.
When Jesus washed my sins away!
He taught me how to watch and pray
And live rejoicing ev'ry day.
Happy day, happy day.
When Jesus washed my sins away!

O happy bond, that seals my vows
To Him who merits all my love!
Let cheerful anthems fill His house,
While to that sacred shrine I move.

'Tis done, this great transaction's done;
I am my Lord's, and He is mine;
He drew me, and I followed on,
Charmed to confess the voice divine.

Now rest, my long-divided heart;
Fixed on this blissful centre, rest;
Nor ever from thy Lord depart,
With Him of every good possessed.

141 REVIVE US AGAIN

We praise Thee, O God,
For the Son of Thy love,
For Jesus who died
And is now gone above.

Refrain

Hallelujah!
Thine the glory,
Hallelujah! Amen!
Hallelujah!
Thine the glory.
Revive us again.

We praise Thee, O God,
For Thy Spirit of light,
Who has shown us our Savior,
And scattered our night.

All glory and praise
To the Lamb that was slain;
Who has borne all our sins
And has cleansed ev'ry stain.

Revive us again;
Fill each heart with Thy love;
May each soul be rekindled
With fire from above.

142 ONWARD, CHRISTIAN SOLDIERS

Onward, Christian soldiers!
Marching as to war,
With the cross of Jesus
Going on before.
Christ, the royal Master,
Leads against the foe,
Forward into battle,
See His banners go!

Chorus

Onward, Christian soldiers!
Marching as to war,
With the cross of Jesus
Going on before.

Like a mighty army
Moves the Church of God;
Brothers, we are treading
Where the saints have trod;
We are not divided,
All one body we,
One in hope and doctrine,
One in charity.

Crowns and thrones may perish,
Kingdoms rise and wane;
But the Church of Jesus
Constant will remain;
Gates of hell can never
'Gainst that Church prevail;
We have Christ's own promise,
Which can never fail.

Onward, then ye people!
Join our happy throng,
Blend with ours your voices
In the triumph song;
Glory, laud, and honor,
Unto Christ the King.
This thro' countless ages
Men and angels sing.

143 THERE IS A FOUNTAIN

There is a fountain filled with blood
Drawn from Immanuel's veins,
And sinners, plunged beneath that flood,
Lose all their guilty stains.

The dying thief rejoiced to see
That fountain in his day;
And there may I, though vile as he,
Wash all my sins away.

Thou dying Lamb, Thy precious blood
Shall never lose its power,
Till all the ransomed Church of God
Are saved, to sin no more.

E'er since by faith I saw the stream
Thy flowing wounds supply,
Redeeming love has been my theme,
And shall be till I die.

Then in a nobler, sweeter song,
I'll sing Thy power to save,
When this poor lisping, stammering tongue
Lies silent in the grave.

144 I LOVE HIM

Gone from my heart the world with all its charm;
Gone are my sins and all that would alarm;
Gone evermore, and by His Grace I know
The precious blood of Jesus cleanses white as snow.

Chorus

I love Him, I love Him.
Because He first loved me,
And purchased my salvation on Calvary's tree.

Once I was lost upon the plains of sin;
Once was a slave to doubts and fears within;
Once was afraid to trust a loving God,
But now my guilt is washed away in Jesus' blood.

Once I was bound, but now I am set free;
Once I was blind, but now the light I see;
Once I was dead, but now in Christ I live,
To tell the world the peace that He alone can give.

145 **BATTLE HYMN OF THE REPUBLIC**

Mine eyes have seen the glory of the coming of the Lord;
He is trampling out the vintage where the grapes of wrath are stored;
He hath loosed the fateful lightning of His terrible swift sword;
His truth is marching on.

I have seen Him in the watch-fires of a hundred circling camps;
They have builded Him an altar in the evening dews and damps;
I can read His righteous sentence by the dim and flaring lamps;
His day is marching on.
He has sounded forth the trumpet that shall never call retreat;
He is sifting out the hearts of men before His judgment seat.
O be swift, my soul, to answer Him! be jubilant, my feet!
Our God is marching on.

In the beauty of the lilies, Christ was born across the sea,
With a glory in His bosom that transfigures you and me;
As He died to make men holy, let us die to make men free;
While God is marching on.

146 **THE SOLID ROCK**

My hope is built on nothing less
Than Jesus' blood and righteousness;
I dare not trust the sweetest frame,
But wholly lean on Jesus' name.

Refrain

On Christ, the solid Rock I stand;
All other ground is sinking sand.
All other ground is sinking sand.

When darkness veils His lovely face,
I rest on His unchanging grace;
In ev'ry high and stormy gale,
My anchor holds within the vale.

His oath, His covenant, His blood
Support me in the whelming flood;
When all around my soul gives way,
He then is all my hope and stay.

When He shall come with trumpet sound,
Oh, may I then in Him be found;
Dressed in His righteousness alone,
Faultless to stand before the throne.

147 **AMERICA**

My country, 'tis of thee,
Sweet land of liberty,
Of thee I sing:
Land where my fathers died,
Land of the pilgrim's pride,
From ev'ry mountain side
Let freedom ring.

My native country thee,
Land of the noble free,
Thy name I love:
I love thy rocks and rills,
Thy woods and templed hills;
My heart with rapture thrills
Like that above.

Let music swell the breeze,
And ring from all the trees
Sweet freedom's song:
Let mortal tongues awake;
Let all that breathe partake;
Let rocks their silence break—
The sound prolong.

Our fathers' God, to Thee
Author of liberty,
To Thee we sing:
Long may our land be bright
With freedom's holy light;
Protect us by Thy might,
Great God, our King.

148 **YIELD NOT TO TEMPTATION**

Yield not to temptation,
For yielding is sin;
Each vict'ry will help you
Some other to win;
Fight manfully onward
Dark passions subdue;
Look ever to Jesus
He'll carry you through.

Chorus

Ask the Savior to help you,
Comfort, strengthen, and keep you;
He is willing to aid you,
He will carry you through.

Shun evil companions,
Bad language disdain;
God's name hold in rev'rence
Nor take it in vain;
Be thoughtful and earnest,
Kind-hearted and true;
Look ever to Jesus
He'll carry you through.

To him that o'ercometh,
God giveth a crown;
Through faith we will conquer
Tho' often cast down;
He who is our Savior,
Our strength will renew;
Look ever to Jesus
He'll carry you through.

149 **COME, THOU FOUNT**

Come, Thou Fount of ev'ry blessing,
Tune my heart to sing Thy grace;
Streams of mercy, never ceasing,
Call for songs of loudest praise.
Praise the mount—I'm fixed upon it,
Mount of Thy redeeming love!
Teach me some melodious sonnet,
Sung by flaming tongues above;

Here I'll raise my Ebenezer;
Hither by Thy help I'm come;
And I hope, by Thy good pleasure,
Safely to arrive at home.
Jesus sought me when a stranger,
Wandering from the fold of God;
He to rescue me from danger,
Interposed His precious blood.

O to grace how great a debtor
Daily I'm constrained to be!
Let Thy goodness, like a fetter,
Bind my wandering heart to Thee.
Prone to wander, Lord, I feel it,
Prone to leave the God I love;
Here's my heart, O take and seal it;
Seal it for Thy courts above.

TABLE OF CONTENTS

A

All Hail, Immanuel..102
All Hail the Power (First Tune) 118
All Hail the Power (Second Tune) ...119
Almost Persuaded .. 95
America 147
A New Name in Glory 56
A Rainbow on the Cloud 63
At the Cross........116
Awakening Chorus...103
A Wonderful Savior. 16

B

Battle Hymn of.....145
Beulah Land 37
Blessed Assurance...121
Blest Be the Tie....137
Brighten the Corner. 46

C

Carry Your Cross with a Smile...... 41
Close to Thee........115
Come, Thou, Almighty King ... 1
Come, Thou Fount...149
Come to Jesus...... 90
Confidence 15

D

Down by the Riverside 111
Drifting 62
Dwelling in Beulah Land 42

E

Even Me 124

F

Faith of our Fathers 77
Fill Me Now........127

G

Like Thine 55
God Will Take Care of You 80
Goodnight and Goodmorning 28

H

Hallelujah! What a..125
He Is Knocking..... 92
He Leadeth Me......122
He Lifted Me........ 4
He Whispers His Love to Me........ 18
Hold the Fort.......117
Holy, Holy, Holy....131
Home of the Soul... 13
How Tedious and.... 76
Hush, Hush 113

I

I Am Coming Home. 91
I Am Praying for You 72
I Am Resolved 84
I Have a Savior..... 14
If Your Heart Keeps Right 52
I Know Whom I Have Believed ... 58
I'll Live for Him.... 96
I Love Him.........144
I'm a Pilgrim....... 35
I Love to Tell the Story 123
I Must Tell Jesus... 3
In the Garden....... 24
I Shall Be Ready.... 47
I Shall See the King 75
Is It the Crowning Day? 23
I Walk With the.... 7

J

Jesus, I My Cross Have Taken 135
Jesus is Calling 83
Jesus, Lover of My Soul 60
Jesus Loves Even Me 97
Jesus Loves Me......101
Jesus, Rose of...... 8
Just as I Am........ 78
Just Outside the....108

K

King of Kings...... 49

L

Let the Joy Overflow 64
Lord, I'm Coming.... 89
Love Found the Way 26
Love Lifted Me...... 40
Loving Kindness ...130

M

Master, The Tempest Is Raging 104
More About Jesus... 11
Mother's Prayers Have Followed Me 69
My Anchor Holds ...107
My Faith Looks Up to Thee 81
My Father Watches Over Me 50
My Jesus, I Love Thee 136
My Savior First of All 38
My Savior's Love ... 71
My Wonderful Dream 19

N

Near the Cross...... 57
Nearer, My God, to Thee 128

O

O Happy Day.......140
O Love That Will Not 32
One Day 66
Only One Way...... 74
Onward, Christian...142
Open My Eyes....... 53
O, That Will Be Glory 6

P

Pass Me Not......... 86
Pentecostal Power .. 79

R

Rescue the Perishing 39
Revive Us Again....141
Ring the Bells of Heaven 132
Rock of Ages....... 82

S

Sail On 105
Saved 70
Savior, More Than Life 114
Since Jesus Came Into My Heart.... 12
Softly and Tenderly. 93
Somebody Cares 59
Song to the Flag....139
Spelling Love 100
Standing in the Need of Prayer 110
Stand Up for Jesus..134
Still Undecided 85
Sweeter as the Years Go By 20
Swing Song 99

T

Take Up Thy Cross. 33
Tell Me the Story of Jesus 29
The Borderland 34
The Church in the Wildwood 106
The End of the Road 27
The Heavenly Stranger 98
The Hem of His Garment 48
The Homeland 44
The Hills Above 10
The King At the.... 21
The Old Rugged.... 9
The Promised Land. 73
The Song of Triumph 2
The Secret of God's Grace 48
The Solid Rock......146
The Son of God......133
The Unclouded Day. 22
There's a Wideness..129
There is a Fountain.143
There is Glory in.... 54
There is Power in the Blood 55
Till the Whole......138
'Tis So Sweet to Trust 31
Transformed 36
Trust and Obey..... 61

W

Wandering Child, O Come Home 109
We Are Marching to Zion 65
Were You There?...112
What a Friend...... 51
What Did He Do?... 45
When They Ring the Golden Bells 5
When We All Get to Heaven 67
Where He Leads Me. 87
Where the Gates.... 25
Where They Never Say Goodbye 30
While Jesus Whispers 94
Whiter Than Snow..126
Why Not Now?..... 88
Wonderful Power ... 68
Wonderful Words of Life 17
Work, For the Night Is Coming 120

Y

Yield Not to.......148